Obsessed

Obsessed

A third volume of autobiography

Ronald Duncan

London
Michael Joseph

First published in Great Britain by Michael Joseph Ltd
52 Bedford Square, London, WC1B 3EF
1977

ISBN 0 7181 1592 9

Phototypeset by
Western Printing Services Ltd, Bristol
and Printed and Bound by Redwood Burn Ltd, Trowbridge and Esher

This book was written with the financial
assistance of the Arts Council of Great Britain.

The author wishes to acknowledge Mrs Valerie Eliot's
permission to publish the letters from T. S. Eliot;
and to thank Lord Harewood for reading and correcting
the manuscript.

For *Virginia*
who asked me to write it

Part One

The Catalyst

Damn, blast and bugger. I don't want to write this. For five years I have been trying not to write this. Why do I do so now? Because I have no option. Because murderers are compelled to return to the scene of their crime. Because grief is a burden, remorse a load which can only be lightened by being carried. And because I promised you that I would write it. I have tried so hard to break that promise.

It was the last time I saw you. You were in bed. I was sitting on the edge of it. For ten minutes, we had not spoken. Not with our lips. Your bruised eyes articulate.

'Do you still love me?'

'Would I be sitting here, if I didn't?'

'No.'

'No.'

Then you turned to a side-table and reached for a book, the second volume of my autobiography, *How to Make Enemies*, published a few weeks before.

'You've only mentioned my name twice, and then on the last page. Why did you do that?'

'As I wrote: "because I hadn't the strength or the courage to write any more." '

'And because you were being discreet?'

'Possibly.'

'Promise me you will write the rest. All of it. I want you to give me that. Promise me.'

You held out both your hands to me.

'I promise,' I said.

At that moment your husband entered the room.

It was the last time we spoke alone. Even so, I did not intend to keep that promise, made under duress. And now that I'm compelled to do so, I write it only for you, though now you can never read it. So it can't help you, it can only undo and damage me. There is justice in that. I can see the risk, but danger never prevented me from doing anything I didn't want to do. Perhaps writing it will bring you back into my life a little. Or more likely, shove me towards your death. Which of us two is dead? It could not be only one of us. You live in my life, I died in your death. Damn you. Those who can be parted never loved.

As for the 'gentle reader', he can take a running jump up himself. I write this for you alone.

I must exonerate you for a start. My life had become a mess before I met you. I saw you as an escape, a window. I did not know that the mess was me. Or that no escape was possible. You tried to save me: it was, of course, you who drowned.

Crabbe, one of my favourite poets, has the line: *Fond of complaint, adverse to relief*. That describes Rose Marie and me at that time. We'd been going through a bad patch, the difficulties of our forties: or, shall we say, mine? I had had a long relationship with Antonia (I will never use that vulgar word *affair*). The best that can be said for me is that I was incapable of being casual. Rose Marie had bent over backwards to live it through, to 'go with it', as her psychiatrist put it, alternating between fits of jealousy and then, when I sulked after throwing the girl out of my life again, reacting by bringing her back to me herself. A pendulum swinging between conventional uxorious disapproval and sophisticated connivance. How I love her for her 'immorality'. Tolerance is the one luxury which is my necessity. If she had loved me less, she might have spitefully abandoned me to my desire. As it was, she clung on; and finally, in order to share my obsession, maintained that she was attracted to the girl herself. I was easily convinced. It made my conscience easier. We set up a *ménage à trois*. So long as the world and its snooping envy was excluded, it worked. The nearest I got to loving my fellow men was to love two girls at once. Gandhi said to me: 'Love should not be possessive.' At least I gave these girls the opportunity to prove it.

Sometimes I wondered whether or not I was merely a catalyst. It was not a question which worried me. But that is how I came to write that three-handed play which caused me to meet you eventually.

George Harewood, who had a ring-side seat at these goings-on at the cottage across his garden, told me not to take Rose Marie's ambivalence or homosexuality seriously. 'She is only feigning it to accommodate you and keep you amused,' he said. Confound our friends when they prove right. I didn't believe him, nor did Rose Marie.

Our friends and children, hearing of the rows, but not participating in the reconciliations, were sure that Rose Marie and I were breaking up. To us this thought was a giggle. We had our secrets. We were not only of one another, we had become one another. And years later when the world had tried to tidy us away into a divorce, a well known Q.C. whom I had briefed and whose father was a judge said, after listening with wide eyes to our marital history: 'If this case comes before my father, I very much doubt that he'll grant a divorce. Being a moral man, he'll probably take the view that you and your wife are better left together, for if separated you might cause havoc to other people.'

It's not often lawyers talk such sense. Those who can divorce were never married. Or that's what I thought at that time – and possibly at this time. The pity is that you were part of that havoc. Though it is difficult to say who was the mover and who was moved.

Oh where do I begin, since this which was us and us which was this doesn't seem to have an end? It's all right for you, lying there in the close embrace of a truly faithful lover, whom I should have seen would eventually supplant me. For how often did you flirt with him, making me jealous of those attractions he held for you, so that even when I clutched you to me, I knew it was he who would hold you in the end? Oh where do I begin now the end is all I have?

No, that is not true. That is a lie. You still run up and down my life. Perhaps that's why I continue to live, pursued by memories, cornered by remorse. But grateful. Grateful for my grief, grateful for this pain. It was you who taught me that life could be measured only by its pain. A man has nothing else to learn. So dare I write this and remember? The alternative is to forget. That's what I've tried to do, failed to do. And if I had succeeded, that would have brought me a pain I could not have borne. Perhaps we cling to the image, when we ourselves have become a shadow. So I will keep my promise. You have been patient with me. Six years you have waited, who has all time to wait.

I can remember nothing of those rehearsals of *The Catalyst* except you. My play bored me unless you were on the stage; and when you were, I didn't know which act you were playing, or care whose words you were speaking. I was content to watch you moving across the stage, my hungry eyes devouring your figure, so boyish from behind, so feminine from the front. That's why, though I distrusted the producer and disliked the production, I attended every rehearsal. It's not often a dramatist conceives a character then finds a player to fit so precisely his imagination. That's what I felt as I saw you as Leone in *The Catalyst*. It had happened to me only once before, when Michael Hordern had played Courtenay in *Stratton*. (That was long time before. You'd have been at your convent then.) When this rare casting does occur, a playwright feels something like a god. Perhaps that's why I looked so sad and remote? I pretended to make rehearsal notes in the stalls. You said I terrified you, sitting there. No doubt you thought I was having profound thoughts, or suffering from a bout of poetic inspiration. I was. I was pondering how I could remove those blue ski-ing pants you wore, which fitted you so decently, or indecently. Seldom has a god concentrated to better purpose, or a poet found more use for his imagination.

I suppose it was because my desire walked out of my eyes that you avoided me, whenever we broke. Or, as I read in your diary after— yes, that is the word, after— 'because he looks so melancholy'. Didn't you guess I was sad only because desire is sad? That's a damn silly question. Of course you knew. Any woman knows. They always know about a man's want before he is aware of it himself. So must you have done. I didn't know that then. The offhand way you treated me at those rehearsals misled me, hurt me and increased my tension. You intended that? Consciously or unconsciously? I'll give you the benefit of the doubt. But the effect was just the same.

I remember running home one day to Orme Square and complaining to George and Marion that I did not know how I could manage to sit through any more rehearsals, because I had fallen in love with you and you were ignoring my existence. They nodded their heads: I thought from sympathy, though perhaps it was boredom. It's strange how we punish our friends. Even so, they didn't rub my nose in the obvious, nor depress me further by stating what I knew. That is Briony's prerogative. As you know, I adore my daughter and always give her the right of way over me, which she inevitably takes as gently as a bull-dozer. It was she who reminded me that you were a film-star aged twenty-one and therefore likely to have other fish to fry than a half-filleted dramatist in his forties.

So I gave you up. For a whole day I abandoned you to your contemporaries, to your admirers, to Virginia Maskell's fans, outside the stage door. That was spiteful of me, wasn't it? But the spite was against myself. Happily, my natural conceit and arrogance came to my rescue. I realised that no lover could come between us, except he who has come between us. As for those rivals, louts who stood outside your dressing-room, I saw them as skittles to be scattered.

But there was one who was always telephoning you. I gathered he was a photographer in his twenties. I overheard the casual way you talked to him. I didn't like the sound of that. I would have been even more apprehensive if I had heard you being rude to him. That is a sure sign of intimacy. But my fears were allayed when I saw him: he was so handsome that the poor oaf was infatuated with himself. His vanity embarrassed you. I have succeeded in forgetting his name.

To celebrate the emergence of my buoyant ego I sent you some gramophone records without a card. Perhaps I didn't know what to put on it. More likely, I wanted to hear you thank the photographer for the gift, though I can't imagine his sending you *Don Carlos*. Then roses, also without a card. 'One of the advantages of being over forty is that you can do or say

the most obvious things without feeling self-conscious.'
Wasn't that from Act II?

After a week's rehearsal, it was palpably clear that you
loathed playing your love-scenes. So did René Asherson.
Consequently both of you came to me after rehearsals for tea
and sympathy. Even so, you were careful never to be left alone
with me. I thought you were frightened of me. How was I to
know you were terrified of yourself? Wisdom comes with age,
and in the spring of 1958 I was only forty-three.

But there was one occasion when you risked it. That was
about a day before the dress rehearsal. Somebody had to
choose a record which would be played when Teresa puts the
gramophone on before her seduction scene with Leone.
Though it is Leone who seduces her. As I say, who was the
mover and who was moved? No one knows where desire
begins.

And so, you volunteered to come with me to choose the
record. We suddenly found ourselves in one of those cubicles
which contain one chair and a gramophone. You had to stand.
You chose two records. I didn't listen to either. They pleased
you, we bought them both.

As I left the shop I remember asking you why you always
wore a crucifix.

'Because I'm a Catholic.'

This should have warned me.

'My wife's a Catholic,' I said.

Yes, this should have warned me. Why is it convent girls are
always such handfuls?

'And you?' you'd asked.

'The devil only knows,' I said.

Religion was hardly uppermost in my mind. I was merely
feeling devout.

'I wish you wouldn't look at me like that,' you said, going
into another shop.

I believed you.

'I'll get a pair of dark glasses.'

You smiled and took me by the hand. It wasn't an amorous
gesture. But there wasn't a bloody hope for either of us after
that. You knew it. I knew it. But we didn't. We wandered

14

down the Charing Cross Road, forgetting where we were going. We actually walked past the Arts Theatre. Do you remember that?

Nor can I forget the snack we had the next day, at an omelette bar behind Leicester Square, just before the dress rehearsal. I can recall that there was a large square candle on the table. Are trivial memories proof that I've a trivial mind? I see you agree. But as we sat there you answered a few of my questions which led only to others. You told me that you'd spent the winter in the Virgin Islands, starring in a film with John Cassavetes; that it hadn't been released yet; that you were under contract to British Lion, who had now leased you to Rank; that it was your third film; and that you loathed all the scripts which were sent to you, and the lecherous and illiterate film producers you had to meet. I could see this wasn't a pose.

I had met many young actresses: pretty, in their platitudinous looks, brassy, and brazen with ambition. You didn't fit. Something intrigued me, I didn't know what it was and I'm not sure I do now. Of course I was attracted to you: 'fixing me with his slow, insistent, sad eyes', as you put it in your diary which I found among your papers five years later when your privacy was assured and our secret had become something of a public scandal.

It was typical of you that just as I got around to accepting your being a film-star you ducked from that category by complaining I hadn't left a big enough tip on the table.

'Ten per cent,' I said, defensively.

'Then please make it fifteen; I was a waitress till a year ago.'

So I left twenty. I could see you liked me for that. You always had the gratitude of a child— it was always so apparent when you were pleased and used to wrinkle up your nose. Your gratitude was gratifying.

So I thought that was an appropriate moment to ask you if you'd come to Orme Lane after the first night. The Harewoods were giving a party.

'Will your wife be there?'

'Of course.'

'I'm longing to meet her.'

15

'Why?'

You looked embarrassed.

'They say *The Catalyst* is largely autobiographical.'

'Do they?'

'They do. Is that why it is banned?'

'Then come to the party to meet her.'

'I can't. I've promised to have supper afterwards with my father.'

'Bring him. And your mother too.'

At this your expression changed. You dropped my hand.

'She won't be coming. They're divorced. They never even meet.'

Pain was apparent on your face. You let me see it briefly. God, how I wish I had weighed that pain in you then, so much of mine might have been avoided. But you were so elusive, so clever at playing hide-and-seek, I could never find you or be certain where you were. Even by the time we'd reached the theatre, you were as gay as a *gamine* again, lugging along your wicker shopping basket, stuffed with aubergines and red peppers which you'd bought at a stall in Rupert Street Market, because their colours attracted you.

Because *The Catalyst* had been banned – to my shame I must be blamed for being one of the precursors of this shoddy period called 'The Permissive Age' – the English Stage Company couldn't present the play at the Royal Court and had made arrangements to do so at the Arts Theatre. As this is a club theatre, the dress rehearsal was open to members. I had brought Rose Marie to it. You had asked me, in your dressing-room before the curtain went up, if she was with me in the stalls.

'Yes.'

'I wish she hadn't come.'

'Why?'

'It's enough having to play opposite her on the stage.'

'What do you mean?'

'It's obvious this play is autobiographical.'

'You shouldn't listen to back-stage gossip.'

'No?'

'No.'

'Isn't it true then?'

'Entirely.'

You were tense, on edge, using your face cream as an ashtray. But I was misled. I'd seen many actresses in that state before a dress rehearsal. I took no notice of it beyond sending you up a quarter bottle of champagne.

I myself never suffer from first-night nerves. I leave those to my relatives. As was usual on such occasions, Rose Marie's hand was clammy. You'd played your scenes perfectly. But I saw my play had been entirely torpedoed. When the house lights went up during the interval, Rose Marie was looking as grim as I was feeling. But I wasn't apprehensive. She knew I had fallen in love with you. But that, at that time, only made us equal. She was playing the game very successfully of avoiding jealousy herself by trying to become the object of it. Perhaps she didn't realise that I could never be made jealous of a woman. Or is that what she did realise? Probably that.

'You're right. Virginia's absolutely perfect,' she said, 'but the man ought to be shot.'

'What can I do?'

'Take your trousers down. The critics will cane you unmercifully.'

I hurried round to your dressing-room.

'What did *she* say?' was all you asked.

We both knew whom you meant. And when I told you it made all the difference to you. You still hadn't met socially.

The mews cottage at Orme Lane was tiny. Consequently our infrequent parties were necessarily small if not select. I can't remember whether this one was ours or the Harewoods'. Probably we'd split it in some way as we often did. The guests were hand-picked with fire-tongs.

George Devine was there. Not as a compliment to me, but to keep in with the 'Earl' as he disparagingly called George behind his back. Whenever they met, which was not infrequently because George was chairman of the Artistic Committee of the English Stage Company, both used to bend over backwards to see each other's point of view, and were thus

17

left prone on their backs on the floor. This posture is known as consensus. I had come to see Devine as a good actor, but as an intellectual phoney.

That evening my genuine hospitality was also extended to the cast of the play which, happily, included the producer and the leading man both in one pair of pants. Two of them would have been too much. René Asherson sat on the edge of her chair looking sad without her husband, Robert Donat, a man I'd always admired but never met. And Gretchen was there of course. But she was Rose Marie's guest.

I myself had been largely instrumental in introducing Rose Marie to Gretchen. I had at first encouraged their friendship because Rose Marie had been very depressed when Antonia had finally snubbed her, and had taken refuge from experience in the conventional burrow of a normal heterosexual relationship which didn't include me either. The reason, I suppose, that I continued to connive at Gretchen's infatuation for Rose Marie was because it endorsed the licence to which I had grown accustomed. No doubt it was all very sophisticated. No doubt. We often trod on each other's toes; at least we tried to avoid stampedes upon each other's feelings. Gretchen's was a colourful personality. In spite of her name, she was not German. She was extremely good looking with a feminine figure; there was nothing 'butch' about her, except her motor-bike. She was affectionate, generous and, within any family, within any week, she managed to make herself entirely indispensable. Even then I saw some of the dangers: how, by pandering to Rose Marie's whims and lessening Rose Marie's dependence on me, she was driving a wedge — but I didn't do anything about it. Largely because, as I've admitted, we'd adopted *quid pro quo* as our motto, and partially because Gretchen made such obvious and pathetic efforts to please that one hadn't the heart to reject her. She knew this, of course. This was her trump card. Consequently I never took a trick.

So, you see, you were my only guest. You came late, your father and an uncle in tow. I suppose the party babbled on for an hour or two. I've no memory of it until the moment when you got up to go. As you did so, something made you stop to

18

tell Rose Marie that on the previous night you'd had a terrible nightmare. Perhaps you did this to excuse your leaving early. Rose Marie was intrigued. Having been psychoanalysed herself, other people's dreams fascinated her. Playfully, or spitefully, she insisted that you told your dream. You said it was about false teeth.

I remember you were standing in the small hall. Your father and uncle had already got their coats on, and were waiting outside by their car. But Rose Marie and you now confronted each other for the first time. Perhaps your dream was an irrelevance you both clung to. All I know is that watching the two of you, I suddenly felt excluded.

'Dreams about false teeth are very sinister indeed,' Rose Marie said jokingly.

At this, you suddenly burst into tears. Everybody was embarrassed. Marion thought you'd had too much champagne. George thought it was the consequence of first-night tension. I was nonplussed. Your tears were not ordinary tears, they were sobs from the depth of your being. You were giving those tears to Rose Marie. And though I'd written the bloody *Catalyst*, and should have twigged, I didn't see then that you were still playing the play. Whether Rose Marie did, I do not know. I suspect she did; her perception about people is always six months ahead of mine.

Your father and uncle were still waiting in the car.

'You'd better go with Virginia, and see she's all right.' Rose Marie said to me.

I told your father that I'd see you home. So they drove off. I found a taxi. You continued to sob in it uncontrollably, quite oblivious of me. I could do nothing to comfort you. I was bewildered by your behaviour. You were not even slightly tipsy. At your basement flat I helped you down the stairs, and steered you into your room. You collapsed on the bed still weeping. Then you fell into something like a trance.

I had never observed anything like that before. I waited, hoping you'd recover, letting you lie there on your divan bed. But you didn't move. Eventually I undressed you entirely. You didn't protest. I found a dressing-gown, managed to put it on you, then somehow bundled you into bed. It never occurred to me to make love to you. That would have been rape — or rather, necrophilia.

I didn't know what to do. I couldn't leave you in that state. I wondered if I should get a doctor. I did better. I telephoned Rose Marie and told her of your condition. She didn't seem surprised.

'Sit with her,' she said. 'She'll be all right. I'm going to bed.'

It was about three a.m. I was tired and your wicker chair was too uncomfortable to sleep in. So I sat, watching you move from dream to dream. I smoked. It got light. Later, I heard milk bottles being moved around. I thought of making a cup of tea. Then you stirred. You got out of bed. For a moment you stood by it. I spoke to you. You didn't reply. You were standing but still quite asleep. Then you sat on the edge of the bed, and with your feet on the floor, lay across it with your head against the wall. I kept still and watched you part your legs, then move your hips, as though copulating with some figure in your dream. I had never witnessed such ecstasy before or contributed less to it. Then I left my chair and woke you.

When you opened your eyes you didn't recognise me. It was clear you hadn't been dreaming about me. Then, finding yourself outside the bed, you were overcome with embarrassment and got back into it, and instantly fell asleep again. You didn't ask me what I was doing there, or how long I had been with you.

I let myself out. On the way home I bought the papers to read my bad reviews. But this was a first night with a difference. The critics and I had not attended the same play.

Most of their notices were frivolous or patronising. As usual I myself 'carried the can', as they say. You and René who'd worked so hard and given such splendid performances were hardly mentioned. The *Daily Mail* carried a large cartoon of Briony, dressed as a convent schoolgirl, carrying a hockey stick on her way to seeing her father's immoral play.

'The Sundays may be more interesting,' I said, trying to console you as you sat in your dressing-room before the second performance.

You didn't care about the reviews. Neither of us mentioned your behaviour the night before. I couldn't believe that it had happened, for you'd recovered so completely. That's what you always did, consequently I never knew where you were. You plied me with questions about Rose Marie and Gretchen. I mistook your curiosity about them for concern over me. A mistake I generally made. But though self-interest is a disease, it is, unhappily, not contagious. We were trying desperately to communicate. But all of our conversations were interrupted soliloquies. I imprisoned in my tangle; you in yours.

'Blind man's buff,' I suddenly said aloud. And then realised that that would be a good title for the four-handed play I'd already started to write; a play which really concerned eight characters, as each one consisted of the person other people saw, and the person he was to himself . . .

'I hated her,' you said vehemently, as a *non sequitur* to my remark.

'Who?'

I had been a long way away.

'Gretchen, of course.'

'You hardly know her.'

'And I don't want to.'

Your ten-minute bell went. I left you to your make-up.

The next day I met Eliot. Though we were both members of the Garrick, we usually lunched at the Étoile. I had sent him *The Catalyst* immediately I'd written it. I had thought he would like it because we had so often discussed the problem of finding an idiom which could carry contemporary sensibility and situations. He'd attempted this in *The Family Reunion* and I in *Stratton*; both of us had overloaded these plays with either Greek or Viennese overtones. But I felt I had at last pulled it off in *The Catalyst*. Indeed, I was very pleased that none of the critics had spotted that the play was written in verse.

I saw Tom was looking embarrassed. Some months before he'd written to me to say that Faber's would decide whether or not to publish when this play received a production. Knowing how difficult it was to sell published plays, more especially verse plays, I thought this proviso not unreasonable. But now I was confident that Faber's would go ahead since the play had received so much publicity because it had been banned.

We discussed Ezra's predicament in Washington as we usually did, and talked about Olga Rudge's efforts to get herself to the States to see him. She'd written repeatedly to us both. Tom seemed sympathetic to her in spite of his long friendship with Dorothy Pound. Knowing something of Tom's rawness about marriage I thought this broadminded of him, and liked him for it. I also treated him as an uncle and confided my own matrimonial tangles and infidelities to him. He had not been unsympathetic there either.

'I didn't want to spoil your luncheon,' he said when the coffee was served, 'so I delayed telling you what my board has decided about this play.'

I knew by his reference to the 'board' that his decision was negative. He always played that one.

I was feeling mischievous. I decided not to let him off the hook.

'Do you yourself think it should be published?'

'No, Ronnie,' he said eventually, looking me straight in the leg, 'I do not. I congratulate you for the verse, but your theme is highly immoral. I don't like the theme at all.'

This last remark was so unusually emphatic I made no comment. I could see that this theme meant more to him than it did to me. Unwittingly the play touched a raw spot. I changed the subject.

Touching raw spots was what this play was always doing. You were affected like everything else. That same evening I came round to your dressing-room after the curtain was down to find you sitting at your dressing-table, still in your costume. You were weeping. Your make-up had run, mascara and Number Five staining your cheeks.

I tried ineffectively to console you.

'But I thought it was a good reception,' I said, thinking it was that which had upset you.

'Why don't you keep your bloody life to yourself,' you exploded, 'instead of plastering it all over London, and then expecting me to play it night after night.'

Oddly enough your angry outburst pleased me. It meant

22

there was some intimacy between us. You wouldn't have shouted at me otherwise.

'Don't grin,' you screamed, throwing some cosmetic at me. 'You can get another actress for your filthy play. I'm not going to be accosted every night.'

'I'll slosh the man,' I said.

'It wasn't a man. But a woman. Three women. They were German girls. They'd seen the play last night, and were waiting to pick me up at the stage door. Lesbians.'

'What did you do?'

'Rushed back in here. Waited till they'd gone away.'

But that was only half of what you did, wasn't it? As I learned. later, much later. You didn't tell me, then, what else had happened. Instead you realised you'd already told me more than was good for you. And so you switched to showing your concern about me. Hide-and-seek. I never knew where you were.

'I think you should see Stephen Rawle,' you said.

'Who's he? An actor?'

'No, a psychiatrist. I think he could help you.'

'I don't need a psychiatrist.'

'That's what everybody says who does. He might straighten you out so that you can one day write something to help people and not destroy them, as this play does.'

That was the second vehement critic I'd found that day. I hadn't expected one to be in my cast.

'And don't sulk. Promise me you'll see Stephen Rawle?'

'All right.'

'Good. Three o'clock tomorrow afternoon. Here's his address. Promise me you'll go?'

'I'd better, since you've made the appointment.'

You threw your arms round me and kissed me. Our first kiss. You were immediately gay, gay with relief and gratitude. I'd have agreed to meet the devil himself for less.

The Catalyst was nearing the end of its run. We were, I remember, in a taxi in Piccadilly when you asked me casually if it was true I had some Arab horses in Devonshire. Of course you knew I had. Hadn't I been using them as bait for days to try to tempt you to come to Mead? But my invitations had always been turned aside.

'How many horses have you?'

'Only four.'

'One I could ride?'

'If you can ride.'

'Couldn't you teach me?'

'If you were in Devon.'

'You see, my new film which is being released in the autumn is very much an outdoor girl picture. It's called *Virgin Island*. We shot it last year in the West Indies.'

'The one with John Cassavetes?'

'Yes.'

Now you'd looked a little shy.

'The publicity people want to take a lot of stills of riding bareback over cliffs and that sort of thing.'

'Then you'd better come to Devon and tell them to bring their cameras.'

'There would be quite a gang.'

'They could have one of the holiday flats.'

'I think I'd have to come down alone to you a few days before they did — so that you could teach me.'

'Give me a week,' I said. 'There's nothing I couldn't teach you.'

'That I didn't mean.'

'I meant even to ride bareback,' I lied.

You'd smiled seeing how happy you'd made me.

'Do you think Rose Marie will mind my coming? I shan't unless she knows, unless it's all right with her.'

'I'm sure she won't mind,' I said emphatically, with several doubts in my mind. 'Anyhow, I promise I'll ask her when I go down to Devon tomorrow. I'll telephone you and tell you what she says.'

'Honestly?'

'Honestly.'

'I don't want to cause trouble between you.'

'There was quite a bit around before I'd even heard of you.'

'But I don't want to be the cause of any more.'

That was, as I remember it, the end of the conversation because we'd arrived at the theatre.

The following evening I told Rose Marie of my *coup*, using a

24

casual approach to cover my excitement. I stressed that the purpose of your visit was wholly because of the publicity photographs. Whether she believed me or not I don't know. Knowing that she knows me, I doubt it. She could always read me like a book, a bad book.

'You'd better not put her on Dil,' she said, thinking of the time when my favourite horse had nearly thrown her over a four-hundred-foot cliff and she'd ended in a bed at the Cottage Hospital.

'No I'll put her on Lucretia.'

'And I suggest you put her publicity agent and his wife down at West Mill studio. The photographers and lighting people can stay at the Hermitage. When is she coming?'

'Nothing's fixed. Virginia said she wouldn't come unless you agreed.'

'Then tell her to come the weekend after next,' she said. 'I shall be spending it up in London. Gretchen has invited me up to her flat. I know how you hate being alone, so you can put me on one train and meet Virginia on another.'

And that is precisely what happened. It was a Friday. I drove Rose Marie to Taunton and saw her off most affectionately on platform 3, then ran under the subway just as your train arrived. You were already walking down the platform carrying that suitcase made of wicker or pampas grass; a thing you'd picked up in the Virgin Islands. An object which rose up to inflict itself on me years later. But I ignored it when I first saw it. I even let you carry it to the car.

Of course, you knew that we were going to be alone. I had told you on the telephone. You seemed piqued, apprehensive that Rose Marie's absence when you arrived meant she had disapproved of your visit. I reassured you, telling you of the arrangements she'd made— putting you in Briony's room and so on, and that she would be returning on Tuesday. So we had a whole weekend to face. I was so excited at the prospect I drove badly. You reprimanded me.

Of course I assumed nothing. I knew nothing about you and what I did know only confused me. Was it because of your Catholic background that I assumed you were a virgin or was it, knowing the utterly insane suggestibility of my mind,

25

because you'd made a film called *Virgin Island*? I don't know. Probably it was because I was attracted to you myself that I couldn't tolerate the idea that anybody else had ever been attracted to you. Or was it that being interested in your future I would not countenance your having a past? Possibly. No. It was your manner. It was modest, reserved and so un-stagelike. I would never have thought of 'touching you up' as they vulgarly but graphically express it.

I can remember nothing of that drive except that you were with me and that I drove fast because I wanted to be alone with you at Mead.

Before I could show you to your room, you ran off to see the horses. It was difficult to make you leave the stables.

We ate but didn't notice what we were eating. Then I built a big log fire in the sitting-room and played the gramophone. *Don Carlos.* It would have been *Don Carlos.* You had sat in the same chair which is opposite me now. I thought you were listening to the music, enjoying the fire. I had no idea what was going through your mind. My own was always sufficient burden. I knew only too well what was going through that. But I behaved myself. You made me feel shy.

Perhaps you saw that? Perhaps that's what made you get up suddenly to say you were too hot. You left the room. Ten minutes later you returned wearing a cotton dressing-gown.

'Now I feel comfortable,' you'd said tucking your feet up under you.

You had surprised me utterly. Ten minutes ago you'd sat as 'still as a glass of milk' as you put it in one of your poems; now you were restless and I knew you wore only a nightdress and the crucifix round your neck. Not wholly surprisingly, I thought this was something of an invitation. I crossed to your chair and kissed you. You received my embrace coldly. I retired wishing I had not made it. I put another record on. Another ten minutes passed. Then suddenly your face changed. You were no longer relaxed. You looked distressed. I thought the change in your mood was due to my clumsy approach or the effect of Verdi.

Then you leant back in your chair and uttered one word loudly:

26

'Cunt.'

I didn't believe my ears. You didn't believe yours, either. You had shocked yourself almost as much as you'd surprised me. Before I could react, you ran out of the room. I thought you'd gone upstairs. I followed. As I opened your bedroom door, I heard the front door slam. I couldn't believe you'd gone out into the dark, cold night wearing only a nightdress and slippers. But that's what you'd done. But which way had you gone? You could have gone so many ways. I never knew where you were. I called your name. I shouted it. Then, remembering the look on your face when you'd heard yourself utter that word involuntarily, I had a sudden intuitive fear that you might have run out to the cliffs. I searched for a torch. Couldn't find one. Eventually I had to fill a lantern. This I knew would have given you a start. Perhaps a fatal one. Then lighting the damn thing I began to run out to the cliffs. The lantern went out. I ran the quarter of a mile calling your name. I went straight to the precipice. You weren't there. Were you beneath it? I ran all the way back deciding to get the car and go down to the beach to look for you beneath the cliff. . . That is how much you had frightened me. Before I got into the car I rushed round the house, even up to your room again to make sure you hadn't returned while I was away. You were nowhere, the house was full of your absence. I ran out again, wondering if you'd gone over to one of the cottages. There you stood by the post box, a figure in a white nightdress, standing absolutely transfixed. You must have been there for half an hour. You were cold. Five minutes more and you'd have collapsed from it. But you seemed unaware. I dragged you back into the house. Gave you a brandy and put you into bed with a hot water bottle. We hardly spoke. I could see you were too exhausted to answer questions. I was too confused to ask them. So I left you and went into my own room.

It was hardly surprising I couldn't sleep. I lay wondering what had made you utter that word involuntarily, and then caused you to react so distressingly. And I recalled your other involuntary act when I had sat in your bedroom in Scarsdale Villas after the first night of *The Catalyst* watching you lie over the bed and make erotic movements in your sleep — no wonder mine now eluded me. So after an hour or two I eventually followed myself back to your room. I lay on your bed, not in it. You pretended to be asleep. I kissed you, I took your hand to give you the reason why I couldn't sleep. Taking the horns by the bull. But you wouldn't let me move your hand. Instead, you took mine beneath the sheet to show me why you couldn't sleep either. That's how it began. From misery to ecstasy within ten minutes. I was surprised your behaviour had seemed so virginal, not that I'd any experience of virginity, except my own.

We'd both needed that, wanting each other since the first day we'd met, crossing a desert of convention thirsty to the oasis which we were. But the more we drank the thirstier we became. It was light before we slept; we rose. And when we did we had breakfast, lunch and tea simultaneously. But you couldn't wait to finish your meal: you ran out to explore every barn on the farm, feeding the calves, collecting eggs and begging me to give you your first riding lesson. You were so happy: I had never seen anybody that happy. Yes, perhaps that's where you were: where enjoyment in simple things are. Within those next few days you gave me more than one present: you gave me not only yourself, you gave my farm to me. You made me see the hens as 'gossiping women with their arms folded behind their backs'; you slid down the hay bales, and taught me to listen to hear the grass grow; your capacity for getting pleasure out of things which I took for granted and failed to notice showed me which of us was the poet. In you, this appetite for life and response to it amounted to reverence. But there was nothing solemn about it: it was genuine reverence: 24-carat joy.

Only once during that day did you look sad, when you said you wished it had not been behind Rose Marie's back. That distressed you more than it worried me, at that time. I couldn't understand you. But it wasn't your conscience, or my own, which was my principle concern. I suppose it could be said that my conscience had had enough exercise to retain its flexibility.

And the next morning I bridled Lucretia and led her out to the big field, Bushellands.

28

'Where's my saddle?' you asked.

'I thought you wanted to learn to ride quickly. Saddles are unnecessary.' I took hold of your shin and helped you to mount, then led you round the field. I myself had been taught by a German cavalry officer. I made you go through the same dull things he'd inflicted on me. You thought I was severe. I was. I showed you how to sit. I told you to grip with your knees, to keep your heels down. And when, to keep your balance, you clutched the reins or the horse's mane, I made you fold your arms behind your back and put a riding crop under your arms, so that you couldn't bring them forward. Then round and round we went, walking; till, when I told you to dismount, you had to slip off because the muscles of your thighs were so exhausted. The next day we trotted and I made you sit it through. You had no alternative without stirrups to support you. And though you fell off a couple of times you came to no harm, without stirrups to catch your feet and drag you. I never saw anybody take to a horse as you did. Within a week we were galloping bareback over the cliffs. We'd already shown the night our hooves.

Rose Marie came back on the Tuesday, driven down in Gretchen's side car. Gretchen was in black, helmeted, her powerful motor-bike like a stallion between her legs. Rose Marie looked wind-blown and scared: a captive pale face hostage to an experience she hadn't enjoyed.

No man, especially me, was likely to have assessed Gretchen accurately. Her appearance was too striking, her manner too charming. She went out of her way to please, to be helpful and, if you weren't careful, she became indispensable. Whenever I mislaid my pen, my spectacles or my cigarette lighter, she looked for them, and found them. You suspected that she had previously hidden them for that purpose. You may have been right. You certainly never liked her. Though I often wondered whether that was because you too found her attractive and were frightened of her influence on you. Perhaps you saw through her divisive intentions and realised that her influence on Rose Marie would be ultimately destructive.

She was, she said, in her thirties. She claimed that she had some West Indian blood in her. Her colouring confirmed it:

Augustus John would have seduced her, Gauguin painted her. That is if they had not been put off by her slouch and her trousers—I don't think I ever saw her in a skirt.

Before her crash helmet was off she was making herself useful about the place, hanging pictures which I'd propped against my study wall for the previous six months. She was the sort of girl— there can't be enough to make a category— who carried fuse wire in her handbag (she had no need for cosmetics) and a screwdriver in her hip pocket. Her handy-man competence made me feel as clumsy as I am with my fingers and more than I care to acknowledge in my habits.

But for all the masculine traits which she affected, I never met a more feminine mind; I use this in its most pejorative sense for Gretchen was especially emancipated from reason. She read *The New Scientist* as regularly as other girls devour *Vogue*. But she had never learned the alphabet of logic. At meals, she would propound some progressive notions at the prospect of which my knees would shake together under the table. In fairness to her, it should be said that such ideas were never her own. She was an intellectual jackdaw who did not hide her trinkets under a floor board. The more one argued with her, the more she held resolutely to a conclusion which neither her argument, or one's own, had led. *Non sequitur* was her *forte*, vehemence was her method: effective, in so far as she succeeded in dominating all conversation as the *Queen Elizabeth* might if berthed in the Serpentine. Gretchen was, you said, a post script from Miss Pankhurst and, I would add, a precursor to Miss Greer. She talked sex as most people refer to the weather and made it appear to me almost as tiresome. With a small independent income she had a credit account at Harrods; and with this personal security I suspected her of being a Party member: or, at least, a subscriber to some comic like *Tribune*.

She had not been in Welcombe a couple of hours before she told me that I reminded her forcibly of Lord Byron; and such is vanity that I found myself assuming she had known that poet. Indeed nothing would have surprised me about Gretchen but the truth. I never discovered what that was. Perhaps she was unhappily a girl without a past and probably she was one without a future, always the indispensable cuckoo in a nest which she always fouled.

Yet for all her failings and absurdities I found myself indulgent towards her. She was pathetic, but never sorry for herself. Indeed she made such a brave effort to impress and cut a figure that one could not help feeling sorry for her oneself.

As for Rose Marie, she was vulnerable. When she was feeling lazy, Gretchen volunteered to fetch or carry; when she sat down, Gretchen placed a gin on one side, a box of chocolates on the other. And she used flattery as a massage. I saw that her influence on Rose Marie was enervating. But Gretchen kept her amused, and since I had become obsessed by you, I did nothing to remove that infection. Influence would have been too weak a word. In this, I failed both Rose Marie and myself. As in everything else, I eventually got the bill. I haven't paid it yet.

Our apprehension disappeared when we saw how Rose Marie had greeted you. She couldn't have been more friendly. *Quid pro quo*, I thought. I never thought enough.

It was Gretchen, not Rose Marie, who asked the question when she and I were briefly alone.

'Well?' she said suggestively.

'Well?' I repeated as if not knowing what she meant, forcing her to reveal a coarseness which came naturally to her.

'Did you make Virginia?'

'I'm always hospitable,' I replied and left it at that. Rose Marie didn't ask because she knew. She knew, because she knew me. She would have noticed instantly that I was happy. And the concern I showed for her would have told her you had given yourself to me. Men are transparent to women. I hadn't been so explicit or obvious as to bring her a present. But in little things I showed immediate consideration which, as any wife knows, is proof that her husband has been unfaithful.

Even so there was no tension. For the next few days, it worked. Gretchen, typically, started doing some carpentry and, not incompetently, doing those jobs which Rose Marie had asked me months or years before to do. While Virginia and I played. That is the word. We played like children. You were thirsty for the country; you squeezed the farm like a lemon. You discovered things I'd lost, toys I'd forgotten. You even introduced me to a bull I did not know I owned.

That, my urchin, was the bond between us. The fact that we played together. Whatever I did you did with me. If I picked gooseberries they were your fingers that felt the thorns. If you were milking, I spilt the bucket. It wasn't my manhood you gave me, something more precious, something which I had lost: my childhood. That was your gift to me: my own child-hood. You had such irrepressible sense of fun, especially with ordinary, simple things.

By the time your press gang arrived at Mead at the end of the week, you could ride even Dil Fireb. But they were not content to take a few stills of you on horseback; they stayed for days down at the Mill. You were photographed in the sea, feeding calves, driving stationary tractors. They thought it made marvellous 'copy'. You were embarrassed by it all. I merely stood around holding the occasional light. Nobody took even a snap shot of me. Dil Fireb and Lucretia preened themselves like stars.

At last this cavalcade departed. I feared you would be going too, since the object of your visit had been completed. It was Rose Marie who asked you to stay. That was generous of her. You needed no persuading.

But because Briony was coming home from her convent for the school holidays, Rose Marie suggested that you now moved out of her room and went down to the studio at West Mill which your publicity mongrels had vacated. Of course there were other bedrooms at Mead. Her suggestion was made not for domestic reasons but to protect Briony from our immoral arrangements which were, by that time, wholly accepted.

I use the word immoral because we were so happy. I've noticed that whenever I was happy, I was certainly being immoral. Perhaps morality and misery are synonymous. But no conventional dictates were imposed on us then. Though we were to be separated at night by half a mile, Gretchen reminded me that there was a double bed in the studio, and that I knew my way down the cliffs even in the dark.

'You'd better be back in the farm in the morning,' Rose

Marie added, thinking of Briony's acquired prejudices, which we call education.

So you moved down into the valley with the beach on your front door and an unspoiled combe stretching for four and a half miles at the back. My favourite place, West Mill: the place I'll haunt if I'm as restless dead as I am alive. Am I? Doubts grow as I write this. Not all the dead are buried. . .

So for the next week or so — it's odd, isn't it, how vague we are about the duration of times when we were happy and how our sadness leaves firmer footprints? — I used to snatch a torch as soon as the house was asleep and run down the cliff path to you. For some bizarre reason I can't recall, I never came in through the door but used to tap on the window. You'd get out of bed in your nightdress to open it. I'd climb in, then you'd hurl your nightdress to the floor. Those were the days, those were the nights. I thank God I've had the strength to sin, as they who have souls of grey call it. Then as soon as the dawn came, I would leave you sleeping, dip my face in the stream and climb the cliffs again. I would make a pot of tea when I reached the farm and take a cup up to every bedroom. Briony used to congratulate me on getting up so early.

Though we were only parted for an hour or two you used to write me little letters so that you could watch me open them to read when I returned. You used to stick a stamp on the envelope frank it and play at being postman too. One of these fell out of a book the other day. I re-read the letter. One phrase in it struck me: 'We'll build a *raft* of love and sail on that — we have plenty of nails.' Now I see where my poem about 'the raft of our desires' came from. . . All poets are thieves: great poets, great thieves. I didn't know I had filched that image.

But there was one memorable morning when I went up the cliff path to the farm and the tea was late. It had been a rough night with heavy rain but the storm outside had only made us cuddle closer. Then, as it got light, I disentangled myself from you and put one foot out of the bed. Something gripped it. Whatever it was it was very cold and slimy. I put my other foot down thinking I must have cramp in the other. Now both feet skidded on slime and I was cold to the knees which wasn't surprising. Our big bed was a raft and the whole studio was

33

two feet deep in dark brown silted water which had flowed in beneath the door, your clothes jetsam or flotsam: everything soaked, tables and chairs, floating. The flood water which had run down the hill, finding the gullies choked, had all been directed into the studio. Like Noah I woke you. Then I ran out naked to divert the flood from continuing to enter the door; and you, similarly attired, began trapping our clothes from floating out of the open door.

When the water had gone we were left with six inches of silt covering the red tiled floor. I didn't know then, but that mess was symbolic of society's reaction to our affection. You began to cry.

'What are you blubbing for?'

'This is the only home we had to ourselves and now look at it.' There's a nesting hen in every woman. I'd already seen you play many parts, but now with a broom sweeping the mud through the door I saw another. What was concerning me more immediately was the choice between two disagreeable alternatives: either returning to the farm stark naked or putting on sodden clothes slippery with mud. I made some disgusting compromise. It took us three whole days to clear up the sludge. You borrowed clothes from Briony. I think you were still wearing them when you were recalled to your bloody studio a day or two later.

I write this without a diary to remind me. So I'm not sure how many days elapsed or nights were endured without my finding some excuse to follow you up to London. Only a few. The best that can be said of me is that I always pursued my temptations relentlessly. I remember you met me at Paddington and how we raced like a couple of kids back to your basement flat, flinging our clothes off almost before we'd closed the door. How we thirsted for each other. The best part of it then was feeling no disapproval, was undivided. Though our love was not holy, at least we were whole. Perhaps there is no difference.

I only stayed a couple of days. Before I left, you said you wanted me to buy you a present, something to console and comfort you when I was gone. For a horrid second I thought you were fishing for some tawdry jewellery. You marched me straight to a toy shop in Kensington saying you wanted a teddy bear to cuddle. Then you chose a panda. I called him Pedro. 'Your deputy,' you said. 'I'll never part with him.' You never did. He was on your bed then. Then, when all I could do was to sit on it, and promise you I'd write this someday.

I can't write any of this today. Because of the date. When it happened, I made up my mind not to remember the actual date. I succeeded. Consequently instead of suffering one day, the whole of January has become a black month. I know it was in January. That I can't forget. If I did my grief would spread over the entire spring.

But the day before yesterday I felt reckless. I went to my 'coffin', the large tin trunk Rose Marie calls my coffin, which I keep in the office, into which I throw all the manuscripts and rough drafts I don't ever want to see again. Your letters and photographs were in there. A whole box file of photographs. And bundles, hundreds of letters. I took them out thinking, if I could find the guts to read them, then that would be one way of getting dates right: when you were here and I was there, and how long . . . But it's no use, I can't find the courage. I am a coward. My life is all pursuit and it is I who pursue and am pursued.

The only thing I can do if I'm to write this, as I promised you I would, is to write what I cannot forget and leave the rest unwritten. I must try to find some mercy for myself. Your letters would have none.

Nor can I remember how long it was before you came down to Welcombe again. It's only unhappiness which carves dates in our minds; those days which were our days went as the wind, leaving no trace. But it couldn't have been long. At that time, there was no parting us for more than a week. My work, and yours too, took second place. That's how it should be: we were born to live, not to work. Perhaps that was our principal achievement at Mead: we made no distinction between leisure and work. We were all very busy doing things we enjoyed. It was that which made you so happy there. If you weren't up to your eyes in paint making the pigsty doors look like a fire station, then you were absorbed for hours discovering a cobble floor buried beneath the old stables at the Hermitage and hoeing round each stone as though it was a precious Epstein or Henry Moore.

It must have been then that Rose Marie decided to do another season of taking paying guests. She persuaded you to stay on to help her. Not that you were much help— you were a fiasco as a cook and so earnest were your endeavours that we always felt constrained to eat your concoctions for fear of offending you. (Do you remember that ghastly invention of cornflakes coated in chocolate and the soggy mess you made? Or that time at Dolphin Square when you asked our accountant, Leslie Periton, to lunch and served liver and bacon with a portion of fried daffodil bulbs which you'd peeled and sliced thinking they were onions? Yet this gourmet too survived to love you.)

You slept in the box room: Rose Marie was playing at making some pin-money and wanted your support. The poor girl always lacked confidence when these ventures materialised. She used to challenge herself with them, I suppose. Your impudence and social cheek was something she could use as a front. At any rate, it worked. The two of you got on like a house on fire. I suppose it wasn't surprising that all that 'ceremony of innocence' was reduced to ash.

The fabric began to singe immediately Gretchen appeared again. She was jealous of the way you and Rose Marie got on. As a trio it worked; as a quartet, it didn't. Her influence was divisive. By subtle insinuations she played upon Rose Marie's Achilles' heel: her lack of confidence, making her doubt herself, and from that, doubt me.

Within a few days of Gretchen's arrival, the festival had become a funeral. I was cast as a philanderer, you as an insensitive mistress who like a cuckoo had imposed yourself in Rose Marie's nest. It was a story with the whole monument of convention to support it. No wonder Rose Marie caved in and now stared, disapproving, at our games. One day, do you remember? I made a solitary and secret journey into Bideford to buy something which I said would give us both pleasure. You'd been intrigued, perhaps a little apprehensive. I gave you your small parcel and, before you could open it, I fired my water pistol full in your pretty face, then ran from your wet revenge.

Like brats we played, you even wore two turkey feathers in your hair, cowboys and Indians. We are dead when we cease to be children. Not all the dead are buried.

But in spite of the June sun, the ice age had moved in. Glaciers of disapproval emanated from Gretchen. Meals which had been gay, friendly, and relaxed became feasts of silence. Gretchen's purpose was to get you out. She'd encouraged your being around at first, because my obvious attraction to you made Rose Marie more vulnerable to her. But now she realised that she'd miscalculated: Rose Marie and you had become close friends who had private jokes from which she was excluded. An old tie still hangs in my dressing-room to remind me how the two of you went into Bideford one day and returned with this gift from you both to me. And didn't you tell me that it had been Rose Marie who had made the suggestion: 'Let's buy our husband a tie'?

But we must not shock the respectable with such immoralities, must we? Let the flag of intolerance fly high from the mast of convention. At this time Gretchen was the standard bearer. She made a somewhat incongruous figure rather as Lenin would have done, with *Hymns Ancient and Modern* sticking out of his hip pocket, urging the Cheltenham Ladies' Conservative Association forward to defend the playing fields of Eton.

But Gretchen was able to conceal her real purpose. Iago should have been a woman. No man can stoop as low, for man is arrested by reason while woman lacks that impediment. When jealousy drives them, and Gretchen was reinforced by envy of your prettiness and charm, they will use any card; if it is not in their hand, they will forge it. No man can be as unscrupulous as a woman. Lacking a man's strength, evolution has put muscle in their tongues. Snakes are not a species of reptile; they are truncated female tongues pursuing their quarry through the undergrowth of gossip.

Rose Marie was vulnerable because, as you knew, as I know, she is lamed with some deepseated insecurity which, when played upon, can make her withdraw even from herself. Her whole personality changes and I had in fact come to call these two personalities by two different names: Mary, the tolerant, giving, happy and immoral girl; Martha, the intolerant, withdrawn, unhappy creature trying desperately to conform to women's magazine ethics. And suddenly, Mary was gone and Martha stood there accusing me of forcing her 'to tolerate the presence of your mistress in my house'. That it had been she who had actually persuaded you to stay was a defence on the tip of my tongue. But women can really forget what it is not convenient to them to remember. And *au fond* my position, our position, was untenable.

An unbearable tension persisted for a few days. It was Gretchen who suggested a round table conference 'to clear the air'. When I heard that phrase I knew we were doomed.

Conventional morality was sure to triumph. We actually did go through the farce of the four of us sitting down round a table. I felt defeated like an old acquaintance of mine, the Sultan of Zanzibar, had been when, chucked out of Africa, he'd tried to settle down in Brighton with a handful of wives.

'This ridiculous situation cannot continue,' Rose Marie had finally said. 'I suggest that you and Virginia move down to West Mill where you can play cowboys and indians and not make me look ridiculous.'

You were hurt; Gretchen looked smug; Rose Marie resolute; I agreed to her terms. At least we were not banished from Welcombe. You and I put our things in a couple of blankets, and moved down the hill that afternoon. We rode down, you on Lucretia, I on Dil Fireb.

But you were so volatile, would wear so many masks, play so many games that by the time we'd dismounted you were quite happy again. Because now you could play at mothers and fathers. By being thrown out, we were suddenly thrown in as it were. You put an apron on and began to cook one of your disgusting stews; while I, cast as the father, was chopping firewood with an axe that wouldn't have cleaved a pound of butter. How you loved improvising, making-do, camping. And though you were bad at it, you were so childlike, so earnest, that your Chaplinesque banquet to which we sat down on our first night broke my heart: a bottle of wine and no corkscrew; a chicken toasted rather than roasted and still undrawn. No wonder you woke with indigestion. I played Lord Rochester's game and pretended to be an apothecary getting out of our damp double bed to gather some herbs by moonlight which I pounded up telling you they would cure you instantly. They did. You were so trusting, so suggestible. Couch grass was my panacea for you.

If I've been happy, it has always been at West Mill. Why? Because as you know, the very situation of the place gives one something and brings out the best in anyone. The idlest man there is soon driven to do something and gets the satisfaction of being useful. You can't live down there without finding yourself digging potatoes, fishing for trout, dragging up driftwood from the beach. Even making a fire becomes an achievement; you become involved with the kettle, a cup of coffee is something you've created. So it wasn't surprising that you were absorbed hanging out your washing on a piece of string.

It wasn't quite so easy for me. . . There were echoes. There were ghosts. Rose Marie and I had first settled there: she with even less than you had, having to wash up without a tap. At least you had a tap, a bathroom and a lavatory. I kept thinking of her as I watched you. So often you put your foot precisely where she had trod. That's why I wasn't as happy as you were. I had more past, more burden. And so I said I'd ride up the hill to the farm to get some milk. I wanted to see how Rose Marie was. I loathed this clear cut amputation. But Rose Marie wasn't there: Martha was. I picked up some milk and retreated.

You tried to cheer me up, to reassure me. The next day you made the mistake of going up to the farm riding Dil herself as if you'd been born on a horse. Half an hour later you returned, tears spurting from your eyes. You'd run to Mary only to find Martha. You were too upset to tell me precisely what had happened. You were destroyed and bewildered. If Rose Marie had been consistently disapproving that would have been understandable, if not acceptable. But she had not been; consequently you felt, as I did, that you'd been trapped. But it wasn't from a sense of injustice that you sobbed, it was because you were hurt.

You said you couldn't stand such sudden disapproval and you were going to leave immediately.

I picked up the telephone finding a courage I didn't know I had, to ask Rose Marie what precisely had happened. Gretchen answered. She pretended not to know. I told her you were distraught and leaving. While I was still talking to her, you suddenly climbed out of the window and ran away. I had known you do something like this before: the first evening you'd spent at Mead. Frightened, I told Gretchen what had happened as it was happening.

'You must go after her,' she said urgently, 'and bring her back.'

I followed you through the same window. I realised that Gretchen's urgency reflected my own but that she had a different reason: if you left, Rose Marie would not be so open to her influence. She would have nothing to console. Though she'd driven us down to West Mill it was not to her book that we should be parted.

I followed the bed of the stream up to the underground pool where we'd once seen a kingfisher. You were there lying on the bank crying. You'd waded up through the pools. Your trousers soaked.

We went back to the cottage and I cooked 'Hell Fire' for you. An Indian dish of fried peas, onions, and elarchi.

I had just succeeded in persuading you to stay, when your agent telephoned. He told you that it was essential for you to return to London immediately because you'd been signed up to do a picture with Peter Sellers. You were furious. You didn't like being bought and sold behind your back.

We rode up the hill, your raffia suitcase on Dil's neck. Then you ran into the farm to say goodbye to Rose Marie and I drove you to the station. On the way, I made you promise to return. You agreed: we promised each other to spend the summer at West Mill. The Sellers picture wouldn't go on location till the autumn at the earliest. By the time we'd reached the station you were talking excitedly of various things you were going to bring to make the cottage more comfortable. I remember these included some new sheets for the double bed, a rolling pin for the pastry you planned to make but never did, and a new Aladdin lamp. You thought you'd be back within a few weeks. I promised to get you some new halters for the horses, to collect some firewood, to ask Bill to sharpen the axe. Then as Robinson Crusoe stood forlorn on the platform, Friday looked out of the carriage with a final demand.

'Write me a poem every day. It need be no more than a post-card.' I did as I was told. Eliot eventually made a selection of these and published them as *The Solitudes*.

I remember he liked the first post-card I sent you particularly:

> Now that we love
>   watch how the world conspires
> To wreck, ruin and upset
>   this raft of our desires;
> Now that we love
>   observe how Time will cheat
> Us of that coinage
>   we do not counterfeit;
> Yet now that we love
>   restrain all tears, just laugh;
> Let joy be our purpose
>   a smile, our epitaph.

As a writer I like to be told what to do. I used to write these post-cards sitting in the greenhouse. To my surprise, after I sent you two or three, you began to write poems to me. These astounded me. I had no idea that you wrote poetry. Possibly you had never done so before. I was arrested by unusual imagery in one of them:

> I waded through a seam of grease
> That arched its back like waves
> While through my hair the scuttle rode
> With the ace and queen of knaves. . .

What sort of a film star was this? Who or what were you? I began to sharpen my pencil.

Just as I used
   to wear your old sweater
Preferring the rag that was yours
   because it was yours
to anything that was mine,

So now I wrap myself
   within this loneliness
Preferring this fact and its cause
   because it is yours
to any dream that was mine.

I began to collect your strange verses. Eventually some were published. I would quote them extensively if I owned their copyright, but I cannot do so.

After you left I went home to Mead. It was pointless for me to go to West Mill till you returned. I could never tolerate my own company. I missed you painfully. I continued to write to you daily. We blessed the man who'd invented the telephone. Roger returned from school; Rose Marie and Gretchen seemed very thick: the latter marching about the place with a hammer in her hand and a mouth full of nails. She was making a bedside table. It's still somewhere in the place. I spent my time writing to you or getting tools and things together for us to take down to West Mill the moment you returned. As for Rose Marie and me: we settled for *quid pro quo*. She saw I was missing you badly and would reassure me that you'd only missed the post if a letter from you didn't arrive.

Somehow I'd managed to endure our parting for a fortnight and had taken a deep breath to swim through the last week. You'd told me you'd bought some sheets, and some kitchen gadgets. Everything was set fair. I had no cause for alarm. During the evenings you'd told me you were seeing a lot of Rachael, a girl friend of yours I'd never met. The only thing I knew about her was that she'd been secretary to Ashley Dukes, the dramatist who was a friend of mine. I was relieved to hear this: it meant you weren't alone, and of course I preferred that your companion was not one of those young men I'd seen outside the stage door. That was foolish of me.

When two women get together, a man should take cover. Of course you'd confided 'my situation' to her: how I was a married man etc., who wouldn't make up his own mind etc. and how complicated things were etc. Consequently you received your friend's advice, didn't you? I should have been warned. All I had noticed that there was a change in the tone of your voice on the telephone. It was as though you were speaking to me with somebody else in the room. And I noticed that you kept asking how I was getting on with Rose Marie and, when I said she was being friendly to me, you'd said sarcastically: 'How very nice for you.' I'd never known you bitchy before.

Even so, I didn't anticipate your ultimatum or understand what had precipitated it. You had told me in the morning that that evening you were going to the première of a new film with Cary Grant in it called *Indiscretion*. I had remarked casually that they'd used the Garrick Club as a setting for one of the scenes. I knew nothing more about the film; if I had I might have been more prepared.

When you did ring very late, I asked you if you'd enjoyed the picture. You didn't answer. You simply said, 'I've decided not to come down to Devon at the end of the week.'

'When are you coming then?'

'Not at all.'

'What d'you mean: not at all?'

'What I say. You must first clarify your life.'

'It's not a consommé.'

'I played your bloody life on the stage, I'm damned if I'm going to live it too.'

'What d'you expect me to do?'

'Choose.'

'A question of "Either or?" ' I asked, daring to quote *The Catalyst*.

You picked up that one smartly.

'Don't give me all that gup,' you said. 'I know the wretched play better than you. I suppose your next bleat will be: "if you like red wine you don't see why you shouldn't like white wine too." '

'Possibly.'

'But though Rose Marie has "the advantage of having a vintage", neither of us are wines, we're women.'

'You don't say?'

There was a long pause. It was you who broke it.

'Ronnie, are you still there?'

'In part.'

'Listen, I love you: I want to be your wife. I don't want to be your mistress.'

'Bigamy?'

'No!' you screamed angry at my facetiousness. 'Divorce. Why can't you get a divorce? Other men do.'

Now I was angry too. You could tell that by my voice. When I'm angry, I don't shout, I whisper.

'Those who can divorce were never married,' I said, daring another quotation.

The phone went dead; you'd cut me off. I tried to ring you back. Line engaged. You'd left the receiver off. Coward.

I hated you then. God knows I was under enough pressure as it was. And you'd surprised me. I didn't expect you to produce the conventional formula, the false equation: if I love you, I can't love anybody else. I was disgusted by this emotional blackmail. You'd shocked me by the ruthless way you'd applied it. And I felt sick. Sick from fear. The fear of losing you.

I found I had wandered into the kitchen. I hadn't noticed, but Roger was sitting alone there having some coffee.

'What's up, Daddy? You look terrible.'

'Virginia has just put a pistol to my head. She says she won't come down here any more unless I ask Rose Marie for a divorce.'

'Bloody women.'

'Bloody women.' I felt close to my son.

'And what d'you want?' he asked.

'Not that. I love Rose Marie. I love Virginia. Divorce would solve nothing. What shall I do?'

My son pondered the matter sympathetically. He felt my anguish. This wasn't the first time he'd seen me in this mess. I suppose the reason why both Rose Marie and I had such splendid relations with our children was that we, being the

44

delinquents, placed them in the position of being tolerant parents towards us.

'If I were you, Daddy,' he said helping himself to my cigarette case, 'I'd let the girl cool her heels for a couple of hours. Then tell her not to be a silly bitch.'

It was sound advice. A couple of hours seemed so long.

Rose Marie had come in. She saw from my expression that something was wrong.

I told her simply that Virginia had telephoned to say she wasn't coming down to West Mill.

'Why?'

'Either or.'

Rose Marie and I could communicate in shorthand.

'I see: put a pistol to you.'

'Precisely.'

'And you don't like that, do you?'

'You know I don't.'

'Anyhow don't look so miserable just because the silly girl's changed her mind.'

'Why not?'

'Because that proves she can change it back again.'

Rose Marie had got a point. I wondered where she'd found such an accurate assessment of feminine psychology. She'd left the room; there was nothing more to be said. *Quod erat demonstrandum.*

So, I went to the telephone again. Now it wasn't engaged. There was no answer. I rang every half hour. Still no answer. I wondered where you were. Then with whom? And doing what? By eleven o'clock I was cuckolded. By midnight I was crucified. By hat pins.

When I did get you to answer, it was nearly one o'clock.

'I've been worried about you,' we both said simultaneously.

'What train shall I meet on Saturday?'

'You sod. Didn't I tell you I'm not coming down?'

'Yes.'

'You sod. You unspeakable sod.'

'I think you'd better come down. We've got so much to talk about. It's not possible on the phone, is it? And . . .'

'And?'

'It would be a pity to waste those new sheets you've bought. I've got a new axe.'

'I'll use it on you.'

'You do that. So I'll meet the 10.30 from Paddington.'

'You're a sod. You're both a shit and a sod. I suppose that's why I love you.'

For the next two days I was happily absorbed playing Robinson Crusoe. Collecting a fairly complete set of tools together which we'd need down at the Mill. Even remembering the new halters and a new blade for the bushman saw. We'd planned to live simply, as self-sufficiently as possible, with the minimum dependence on shops and the farm. For fuel, beachwood; I'd bought a new fishing line to catch trout from the stream. You'd instructed me to get whole meal flour and yeast: though, in fact, we lacked a stove except the old clomb oven which had to be filled with gorse which was burned *in situ*, then raked out with a wet broom leaving the clay walls glowing. We'd used it once. It took a day's work to bake some bread . . . I remember I also bought a coil of rope. What could that have been for? I've no idea.

Rose Marie watched me load up the jeep with these and other bits and pieces which I'd picked up on the chance they might come in useful, with amused indulgence. She'd never thought of me as a handy-man.

'You're going to be busy,' she said. 'Don't forget some paraffin and a couple of spades. Or are *you* going to do all the digging?'

When I met you you were staggering along the platform with a parcel under each arm and a packet in your mouth. You'd bought your new linen sheets, some coffee from Fortnum's and some curtain material, though you admitted to forgetting to buy any cotton or needles. You hoped that Rose Marie would lend you these, as the curtains would be hers anyhow.

Your reception at the farm was polite, no more. We scuttled down the hill too happy at being together to worry much about anything else. I have tried so hard to forget what your first action was when you entered the cottage. Before I had

46

carried in all the stuff from the jeep you were down on your hands and knees on the floor turning out the bowels of the old white kitchen cupboard. It was full of old saucepans, boot polish, and junk of every description. That was just one of the things about you I never understood: you were the untidiest person in the world with your own things; you never filed a paper or a contract. Your underclothes were shoved in balls in your drawers, your stockings were single, never in pairs; the inside of your handbags looked like a jackdaw's cache. Yet for all that there was nothing you enjoyed more than tidying up Rose Marie's cupboards. Do you remember how you spent a whole day going through her mending cupboard, sorting all her buttons and reels of cotton into different sizes and colours, then putting them in tins, labelling each so methodically? Those tins still carry your scribble on them. I saw Rose Marie using one only the other day. And so, at West Mill you had everything out of that cupboard which hadn't been cleared out for fifteen years. Then you began to knock nails into the inside of the doors, hanging our set of tools on them: the axe, the hammer and the chisels on one side, the saw, the pinchers, the pliers on another. This was the sort of thing you did which broke my heart. You had the earnestness of a child. I suppose that's what innocence is. Afterwards I couldn't bear to open that cupboard again. That's one of the reasons I had it removed.

Once we'd got ourselves ship-shape, you put on a pretty apron and played at getting the dinner. Neither of us noticed what we ate which is just as well, you say, since you'd cooked it. I insisted on making the coffee then cursed because we'd forgotten a strainer. But what did *things* matter? No *thing* matters.

And we were too happy the next day, or the one which followed, for me to remember what we did or where we loved. It wouldn't have been in bed: you thought that too obvious.

Then just as we were learning to manage, your wretched agent telephoned to say it was essential that you returned to London. I cursed him, I cursed you. Then my anger became somewhat subdued because my own agent, Margery Vosper, phoned me to say that she had just sold an option for the film rights of *The Catalyst* to some Hollywood tycoon, and that it was imperative that I came to London the next day to talk to him since he was only going to be there twenty hours. So that was that. We both felt indignant and foolish. Like two happy castaways rescued unwillingly by helicopter.

I telephoned Rose Marie to give her the good news. Margery Vosper had told me that $1500 had already been paid for a six months' option and $50,000 would be paid if the film went ahead.

'I am so glad,' she said joylessly.

'So will you drive Virginia and me to the station in the morning?'

'Gladly.'

I didn't like the sound of that. The next morning, we went up to the farm. Gretchen was waiting ready to drive my car into the station. While you packed your case I went to say goodbye to Rose Marie. She was up in our bedroom.

'As I told you,' I said, 'Margery Vosper wants me to go up to see a film producer. He's only going to be in London till tomorrow night. I'm seeing him this evening. I'll be back in a day or two.'

She said nothing. She looked at me with slow eyes. Then she hurried away. Gretchen sounded the horn. We'd only half an hour to get to Bideford to catch the train.

Gretchen was cheerful as she drove us in. Too cheerful.

As the train pulled out of the station, I began an ache of apprehension. What did Rose Marie's look imply? She couldn't have thought that my story about the film rights was invented, so that I could go off with you. Or could she?

'Maybe she thinks we've eloped,' you said mischievously. Then seeing I was miserable you suggested I telephoned Rose Marie as soon as we reached London.

I was in anguish all that journey. I telephoned immediately I arrived. There was no reply. So I wrote her a note and sent her a present of a gramophone record: Kurt Weill's *Threepenny Opera*. I wonder what made me choose that? Probably because I knew she liked it. Now I felt divided. I didn't know where I wanted to be. I didn't know with whom I wanted to be. I was happiest if you and Rose Marie were together and I was in the next room. Only then could I experience that solitude which is not loneliness, and be whole, and not divided in part. Fit for a nut house? Indubitably.

Scarsdale Villas. I think it was number eight. A basement flat. Rent eight pounds per week. Your bedroom looked out onto a dustbin and some steps which ran up to the level of the street. We had had a happy night, cuddled up in your single bed. Even so I woke early. I always do. First I saw his boots descending the steps, then his shabby raincoat, his valise, his tobacco-stained moustache, then finally his bowler hat which passed above the window's net curtain, dissociated from its owner, as though floating on the sea. There was an imperious and insolent rat-tat on the door.

'Can't be the milkman. I've paid the milkman.'

'It can't be the postman.'

'Too early for the post.'

Then the floating bowler reappeared. Suddenly it was raised three inches above the curtain. Two small eyes appeared beneath it. They peered down at us in the bed.

'I think we are being observed,' I said.

Then the hat sank again as the owner found the strain of standing on tip-toe too much for him. There was another sharp rap on the front door. Now more insolent with the tone of disapproval.

'You'd better go to see what Peeping Tom wants.'

I never wear pyjamas. I put on your flowery silk, embroidered dressing-gown and went to open the front door.

'Mr Duncan?' the moustache asked. 'Mr Ronald Duncan?' the tiny eyes repeated.

'Yes.'

'I have observed that you have passed the night in these quarters.'

'What's that to do with you?'

He brought his brief case up to the ready. Opened the brass latch and produced a long envelope which he thrust aggressively into my hands.

'It is my duty to serve this on you.'

Then the bowler scurried up the steps.

The envelope bore my name. A writ. I wasn't aware that any of my debts had reached that stage. I thrust the envelope into your dressing-gown pocket and went down the dingy passage back to the bedroom.

'He was a sort of debt collector I suppose,' I said. 'He pushed this at me.'

It was from a firm of solicitors. I opened it. I couldn't believe what I read. No small debt had I overlooked. I was being petitioned for divorce. The bowler hat, a representative of a private detective agency would provide the necessary evidence. Miss Maskell would be named.

I was stunned. I felt betrayed. I couldn't believe Rose Marie had sunk to use the law against me, behind my back as it were. Had she not suggested you and I should share a room at Mead? What need had she of Messrs Smellie or the bowler hat?

For five whole minutes, I stood there looking at this beastly paper. You sat up in bed looking at me.

'But isn't this what you wanted?' you asked.

I made no reply.

I can't remember my movements during the rest of that day, only the pain of it. I remember hurrying round to Orme Lane where my mother and sister were staying with Briony. I showed them the letter from the solicitors. Briony too had had a letter from Rose Marie to tell her that she had decided to divorce me and had already left Welcombe.

'Where is she?'

Briony didn't know. She began to cry.

She'll be with Gretchen,' my sister said spitefully and accurately.

I telephoned the solicitors and naively asked them where my wife was. 'It is not our custom to release our client's address.'

'But your client is my wife,' I bellowed.

'Perhaps you should have thought of that before,' the voice remarked and put the telephone down on me.

Panic. The very notion that Rose Marie could walk out of my life was something I had never imagined.

'But now it's occurred,' my sister reminded me.

. The second post to Orme Lane brought another letter from Rose Marie's solicitors. It listed various possessions of hers at Orme Lane, including clothes and books, which I was instructed to leave at their office in Adelaide Street. And in addition, the letter went on, 'Mrs Duncan would like you to deliver her parsley-cutter which she inadvertently forgot to take with her when she left Welcombe.'

This mention of a ridiculous parsley-cutter touched me deeply. That was typical of her. She knew it is such little things which hurt. Rose Marie always had a mania for collecting kitchen gadgets: I had brought her back mincing-machines from New York, egg whisks from France and this silly parsley-cutter from Milan. It consisted of a series of rotating discs beneath a plastic cover which fitted into the palm of a hand. Rose Marie had been delighted with it. She prized it more than any jewellery I'd ever given her. That which I had, she had never worn. Now, the bloody parsley-cutter was the one object, apart from the grand piano which Britten had chosen for her, which she wanted from Mead.

I think I met you for lunch. I have a feeling that meal was a failure. You saw I was upset and that not unnaturally upset you too. But you trod carefully.

'It's all Gretchen's fault,' you said, echoing my sister.

I decided to catch the midnight train to Devon. Briony volunteered to accompany me. Her mother had told her in her letter that she'd left the car at a garage in Bideford. The journey was cold: the journey was miserable. Neither of us slept. Both of us worried. We reached Bideford at dawn and walked the streets for an hour before we could find a cup of tea from a pull-up for lorry drivers. Then, when the garage opened, I retrieved the car and drove out to Welcombe.

A quick glance round the house showed Rose Marie's departure had been carefully planned and premeditated. Indeed, all her clothes and so forth had gone. Amongst my mail there was a bill showing that they had been packed in new suitcases purchased on my account at the saddler's. I thought that petty.

'That would be Gretchen's idea,' Briony said.

Nobody would dare blame Rose Marie to me.

The house was empty. The chair was empty. The bed a slap in my face.

'We'll have to find her,' I said.

Then it occurred to me that she might be hiding in another house at Welcombe: at West Mill, or the Hermitage. I rushed there. They were all empty.

Briony and I discovered our beds were damp. We lit a fire in the sitting room and slept in front of it, on the floor.

The next morning my impulse was to run from the house she had emptied of everything but her absence.

A month before Rose Marie and I had decided to build a wall ourselves in the garden. We had both spent an afternoon dragging stones up from the bed of the stream and loading them into the boot of the car. We'd enjoyed doing that. It was to be very much our wall, something we'd build ourselves together. Now the pile of flat stones still with moss on them mocked me, hurt me. I hurriedly gave some instructions to the farm manager and drove off. I didn't care if the whole place slithered there and then off the cliff.

I was acutely miserable. I had often had the experience of a girl friend leaving me, never a wife. This was intolerable, not to be tolerated. Briony was almost as upset as I. That evening I drove to Harrow to tell her brother. He didn't seem particularly surprised or distressed.

'She thought that's what you wanted,' he said. 'If it isn't, she'll come back. After all, she'll soon get bored after living the life you've led her.'

I glanced at his straw hat. He had no right to pretend to be a schoolboy.

And though nobody, apparently, believed us, and Rose Marie thought we'd eloped — or Gretchen gave that suspicion — we did each have those two summonses to London about films. You were always on that string. But for me it hadn't happened since Gabriel Pascal had died. This new Hollywood tycoon who had tied up to my little jetty had made quite a name with a film called *The Big Knife* which I hadn't seen. But you said it was impressive. My agent was delighted he'd bought an option on *The Catalyst*. He received me in some bijou mews cottage behind Harrods. He told me that Simone Signoret had agreed to play Teresa; and he wanted William Holden to play Charles. Naturally I wanted you to play Leone again. But he said he had already cast some star who was in the ascendant at that time who would be getting a quarter of a million for the picture. My interest in this interview was twofold: to try to avoid the bourbon; and, at the same time, land the job of writing the film script of my own play. I succeeded only in the first. He told me bluntly that my play which I'd written 'as an exercise in economy' in one set for three characters, needed 'opening out' if it was to be a film. 'Consequently,' he said, 'I have commissioned the two smartest script writers in Hollywood to do the job.' I asked if I would be allowed to read it and, to my surprise, he said he had no objection.

We met after our respective appointments; both equally depressed. The script you'd been given read like a roll of Bronco, but was less flexible. Your only consolation was that you'd be playing with Peter Sellers. But you had no choice: your contract was inflexible. You had less option, you used to say, 'than a whore'. And I wasn't feeling particularly cheerful thinking of what Messrs Sol Fartasse and Art Richovoske, the two smartest alecs of Sunset Boulevard, would do to my play. The only thing I could do was to emulate both Pontius Pilate and Mrs Porter and wash my hands and feet in soda water.

Because my mother and sister were still staying at Orme Lane, on one of their rare visits to London, and Briony was also there, there was no room for me anywhere at that tiny mews cottage. Not that I needed any excuse to stay with you at Scarsdale Villas. But my mother told you she thought that it was very kind of you in the circumstances to put me up on a camp bed in your sitting-room. You thought she really believed that. That was silly of you. She was an Edwardian: both broadminded and discreet. Not like we are today: open-minded, coarse, tactless, clumsy.

Part Two

The Pendulum

It is one thing to lose one's wife: quite another, to misplace her. That Rose Marie had gone off, reduced me to panic and despair; that she had apparently betrayed our tolerant *modus vivendi* by reverting to conventional morality by having me trailed by Messrs Smellie and Co., then producing the trump card of a petition, made me feel that it was she who had been unfaithful — not in the conjugal sense, but worse — to the 'immoral' understanding which we had so carefully nurtured between us. These thoughts bewildered and confused me. But to top this mental distress, she had done something which she must have known would sink me completely: she had disappeared. She knew how impatient and irritated I always became when ever I misplaced my diary, my pen, my cigarette case or my lighter. I knew that by deliberately misplacing herself and hiding from me, she was not seeking privacy, but calculating on the mental effect her disappearance would have. I hadn't the faintest idea where she had gone. Her solicitors had, rightly, refused to give me her address. Her bank did likewise. I felt foolish, too, like a man who can't find his railway ticket, or has momentarily forgotten his identity. Rose Marie and I had been so close for twenty-five years, her disappearance was amputation to me. If I hadn't always made it clear to her, there had never been any doubt in my mind—which is more important— that I loved her. True, I had been unfaithful as the world measures faith, but that was partially an expression of the depth, the measurement of our affection. We had, I thought, security which allowed laxity within it, an essential closeness which permitted flexibility. Or so I thought, or so I thought. But events/sometimes disrupt our thoughts. And in this state of mental anguish, I had driven back to London with Briony asking her questions she couldn't answer and answering questions she didn't ask.

And Rose Marie's disappearance castrated me in a more fundamental sense. I am nothing if not a writer. How could I write to her if I didn't know her address? I was reduced to impotence; for a poet, being deprived, the loss of his pen is worse than the failure of his penis — no wonder, they derive from the same root.

Such was my disturbed state of mind when I returned to London. You consoled me, you comforted me; and I remember you refused to allow me to blame Rose Marie for either her disappearance, for putting detectives on me to peep through your privacy, or for issuing this nasty petition. 'These are all Gretchen's games,' you said. And I, by believing you, now found myself more emotionally divided than I cared to admit; but which you, with feminine perspicacity, easily observed. What you saw hurt you, but you kept that hurt to yourself.

Naturally, I ran to George and Marion with my troubles. They were sympathetic and even went so far as to feign surprise that any storm should have swept me from my happy and wayward course though they must have seen that coming, unless heaven itself had a special focus upon me. George told me not to worry about Rose Marie's disappearance. 'If you're playing hide-and-seek and nobody finds you, you have to pop out sooner or later or you're in for a dull evening in a cupboard.'

Britten, my other close friend, wrote a note saying he'd heard from Roger that Rose Marie and I were going to be divorced and he thought that would 'tidy' up the situation. I replied rather tersely: 'It is I who is being tidied away.'

I am quite unable now to describe the emotional and mental distress I experienced at this time. Toothache of the mind; a carpenter's plane caressing my testicles; anger that the ethics of Tooting had triumphed over me; fury that all the delicious chaos I had contrived had now been hoovered away, reducing us to a simple title: *Duncan v. Duncan*.

For several days I carried this beastly petition around in my pocket, occasionally producing it to glare at it with distaste. Odd perhaps, that though I should have resisted marriage to Rose Marie so strenuously, divorce should have given me such an affront. But not if you think of it: I knew marriage was paper and divorce was paper too; that paper couldn't join us, nor paper separate us.

And now, sitting before the desk of my solicitors, Gilderstein and Bash, I saw a sea of paper suddenly engulfing me.

Anthony Gilderstein informed me that his sister was the partner in the firm who specialised in divorce. He took me to her. Having introduced us, he left the room. She opened a new file and sharpened a Venus pencil, inappropriately, I thought. Then she looked at me with feminine contempt veiled behind professional disdain.

'I presume that you are not going to contest this petition and that the facts are as stated, that you committed adultery with Miss Valerie Musket.'

'Virginia Maskell,' I corrected.

'Quite so. On the 21st instant at 8 Scarsdale Villas.'

'There were other occasions. . .'

'No doubt,' she said acidly. 'One will do.'

'For whom?'

She was not amused. As *Solicitor v Client*, we established a relationship similar to sodium and water.

Our first interview was brief. She asked me to prepare a list of my assets and income informing me maliciously that Rose Marie would obtain one-fifth of my capital and one-third of my income. And she said, rising to her feet: 'I shall require a statement from you describing your married life and what led to its breakdown.'

From her tone I gathered she would read the document with the relish of a vegetarian attending Smithfield Market.

If you remember I wrote it as honestly and as briefly as I could. You read it. To try and make me smile you offered to buy the film rights. . .

But Miss Gilderstein was not amused. She was shocked. Visibly thrown.

'Do you mean to say that you've committed adultery with half a dozen different people?'

'They were all women.' I hoped this mitigated my offence. It didn't.

Miss Gilderstein viewed her client with marked distaste. As a spinster of forty, she had, I suppose, every reason to resent somebody whose philandering had been so extensive yet somehow had excluded her. And when I told her that though I was living with you I did not want a divorce, she could not understand.

'You can't be in love with both your mistress and your wife,' she said, as though quoting from Hailsham.

'Why not?'

'Why not! I like both red wine and white wine,' I replied, this time quoting myself.

She now regarded me as a drunkard too. . .

After half a dozen interviews of this kind, I became aware that since I couldn't change my spots I'd better change my solicitor.

I told Britten of my legal tangle. He advised me to go to his people whom I came to refer to as Messrs Foreskin, Tickle and Bollocks. With them at least I had a man to talk to and less disapproval to pay for. But I could not conceal my utter contempt for the law which I regarded as clumsy, divisive and frivolous. Not unnaturally my misery at Rose Marie's disappearance and my anger at being sued for divorce had its effect on you. My reactions had surprised you and hurt you. You tried to hide these feelings from me. Then one ghastly evening we decided to have it out, as they say.

You asked the questions, I tried to evade the answers.

But eventually I was driven to admit that I wanted to get Rose Marie back, I was worried for her in relation to Gretchen and that I certainly did not want a divorce. Your reaction to this was to say that in that case there was no future for us. I didn't comment. I was tired of the either/or syndrome, of being filed away. You took my silence for agreement. 'So we'd better part,' you said, 'and if we're going to part, let's do it quickly. It's painful to have a leg amputated by the gums of a toothless mouse.'

'Do you refer to me?'

'No. But if we've no future, we can't have a present either. So we'd better part.'

'You may as well say we'd better die.'

'I mean it.'

'When?'

'Tonight. Let this evening be our last. Then Rose Marie will come back. She'll drop the divorce and you two will live happily ever after.'

'Don't be unkind.'

'Who's being unkind?'

'I'm sorry.'

'I detest you when you apologise. . .'

You became angry. You always did when I said I was sorry. Then you came to sit on my knee.

'Can't you see I can't bear to see you unhappy: and I don't want to be the cause of making two people I love unhappy. I'm the cuckoo, so I'm getting out.'

'Don't be silly.'

I didn't believe you meant it.

'So let's go to bed and make love for the last time.'

I kicked my shoes off. Now I was sure you didn't mean it.

'Then you can take me round the corner, give me a drink at the pub and we'll never see each other again.'

But your tears hadn't convinced me. I kissed them away.

An hour later you raised your sleepy head and said: 'Now how about that drink you promised me.'

'What drink?'

'Our last, don't you remember?'

You were already dressing. A look of quiet determination on your face. Like a child who was plucking up the courage to go back to school.

We walked hand in hand to the Earl's Court road and went into a pub. I remember there was a florist next door. I bought you a flower. Then we went into an empty bar and you bought me a Horse's Neck.

We sat in silence. I could see you were playing it for serious. I always went along with your games and never knew when they were true. Now as I sat there I became persuaded, too, that perhaps it was best for us to part. I was becoming a convert to that creed of either/or which I detested. Perhaps I hadn't the strength to fight any more. Perhaps I knew that I couldn't face the unhappiness I had caused you.

'I shall sign that contract and go to America and do a film there,' you said. 'Promise me something.'

'What?'

'Not to look round,' you said, getting to your feet.

We went outside. We stood on the pavement looking at each other, not saying a word with our lips. Tears ran down your cheek. Then you kissed me. 'Please don't write, telephone or try to see me. It's going to be difficult, don't make it impossible.' Then you ran across the street oblivious of the traffic. I stood there and watched you go. This was it. I stood and watched you go. I didn't run after you. Perhaps you thought that was what I would do? But I had lost all my will. Parting from you had stunned me. It now thundered in my head; *it rained behind my eyes*. I stood where I had stood. I couldn't believe it had happened or that I had let it happen. I told myself that I must have wanted it. So, I tried to feel the relief of a decision. I couldn't find any. Slowly I walked away. I had nowhere to go. It took me a long time to get there. I wandered the streets, already looking for you. After an hour I found myself in Hyde Park, passing a phone box. What's the point of a promise if you can't break it?

I rang you.

The unanswered bell perforated me. Where were you? And with whom? I was jealous, suspicious and suddenly panicked. I could not bear the loss of you knowing we did not wish to part but had been manoeuvred into this amputation. Nothing that parted us could be sense. But as I wandered on, I knew that you had gone, that I had deserved to lose you. How could I expect you to live as a weekend girl loving me as completely as you did? How could I be so cruel to you? Better to be cruel to myself, I said, and bear the loss of you than make you suffer from a life I could not complete.

For the next four hours I walked the streets going nowhere, nor knowing where I was. I saw that I had behaved atrociously, selfishly towards you: making you dependent on me,

62

yet remaining independent myself. I realised I had to let you go, since my attachment to Rose Marie made it impossible for me to be complete with you. Indeed I became a belated convert to the conventional morality I had despised. I resolved to put my past behind me even if it deprived me of any future. I would let you go: let you find a man of your own: young, handsome tall, clean, and of your own age who would court you devotedly, marry you romantically, then give you a house in Uxbridge, two cars, three children and a television set. I began to ponder what would be an appropriate wedding present. Now feeling like St Sebastian crucified on my own resolution, I realised that I had been walking the streets for five hours. It was one o'clock. I had not eaten. I had nowhere to sleep. I decided I had better go to Boodles. I stood at the top of Kensington Church Street looking for a taxi. None came by. I moved towards a traffic light and waited there for fifteen minutes or more. I was feeling cold and desperate. I could see myself spending the night in a telephone box as I had done once before. Then eventually a single taxi drove down the road and stopped at the lights. I ran towards it, opened the door and saw you sitting in it. Both of us believed we were seeing a ghost. Of all the thousands of taxis in London driving down all the hundreds of streets why had I to pounce on yours?

'Don't stand there,' you said, 'get in. Have you been waiting there all the evening?'

'No. Dammit. This undoes me. I had made up my mind never to see you again.'

'So had I.'

'Where have you been?'

'What's that to you?'

'Nothing of course.'

'Of course.'

The taxi had been standing outside your flat for five minutes before we disentangled. The cabby discreetly knocked on the glass.

'I'll take it on.'

'Where to?'

'Boodles.'

'To hell you do,' you said, hauling me out. 'If we can part once for ever, what's to stop us doing it again?'

It was about this time that you made a remark which disturbed me. In retrospect I should have taken it as an alarm bell ... I don't recall how the matter had come up. But one day you calmly announced to my own face that I had written *The Catalyst* about you. How the hell could I have done that since I'd never even heard of you until we came to cast it? Clearly you had succeeded in identifying yourself so completely with your part in the play, that you had become Leone and had ousted Antonia, on whom I had modelled that part. Your assertion silenced me. I should have done something about it. I don't know what. I did tell our analyst. He made a note. That's all they ever do. Somebody should have sent for a fire engine. I let you down there. I didn't know what to do.

Strangely enough, one of my happiest interludes now occurred. Happiness is not the right word; I was miserable throughout it. But the memory of the misery has faded, the recollection of the closeness I found with Briony remains. My mother and sister had returned to Devon; Rose Marie was incommunicado; Roger was still at school; Briony was attending the Triangle Secretarial College. I could not let her live alone in the Harewood's cottage in Orme Lane, so I moved from your flat in Scarsdale Villas to be with her. This arrangement was for only a few weeks until I could find a flat because I had promised Marion to vacate the cottage.

Briony used to go off to her school in the morning and then return about five o'clock. It was too late for her to do any shopping then. So, I found myself having to be both mother and father to her. When I was sitting at my desk through the day, I was not composing poetry, but shopping lists and menus for her dinner. I'd discovered that there was no delicacy you could not buy either in Whiteley's or in one of Queensway's shops. As George drove off to Covent Garden, he would observe me wandering off with a shopping basket. When he returned, I was often wearing an apron. Briony and I dined on *moules*, scallops *provençals*, partridge or woodcock. My big-

64

gest culinary triumph was a blackberry and apple pie. The puff pastry was perfect. A small thing, no doubt. But in retrospect, I know it is these little things which count.

After Marion had asked me to vacate Orme Lane so that her mother, Sophie, could move into the cottage, I had no place in London. I had to provide Roger and Briony and myself with a roof. Your flat wasn't big enough. I didn't know where Rose Marie was or I might have posted the children to her.

Britten, knowing of my predicament, immediately offered me his house on the front at Aldeburgh together with his invaluable housekeeper, Mrs Hudson, to look after us. He and Peter Pears, were off on a continental tour. I accepted gratefully. I was particularly touched by Ben's offer because I knew that he didn't approve of my relationship with you; he was fond of Rose Marie and had known her as long as I had.

Mrs Hudson mothered us; we went fishing with Billy; Roger did his pathetic best to keep me cheerful and by his efforts made me feel more sad; Briony tried to interest me in the local antique shops. I bought a pair of Georgian silver candlesticks, not for you but for Rose Marie.

A soft scarf of a mist hung every day over the cliffless coast. The flatness of Suffolk had often depressed me. The very sound of the word 'mere' makes me miserable. A *Peter Grimes* foghorn sounded repeatedly, ominously, like Doom. Melancholy seeped through me, a depression cemented me together. Perhaps because I was living in Ben's house, I started to sketch a libretto on *Lear*, Pears to sing the Fool. I didn't get very far. I burned it.

Then I heard from my agent that I had to be in London for some rehearsals so we left Aldeburgh. I planned to get a furnished flat for the three of us. I thought this would be easy. I had no idea. Briony and I drove round with agents' lists in our hands, she becoming outraged, I impatient, as we peered into one grubby and scruffy tenement after another. They were all filled with knick-knacks, carefully furnished with bad taste. Eventually we were too exhausted to look further and took a damp dungeon in Cheyne Row which was on the second floor. We were cramped. This was the era of living in suitcases;

by, with and from suitcases. Days when I couldn't find a clean shirt because I had sent them all to the laundry, and forgotten which laundry. Suits were likewise deposited by me at cleaners where they still remain. I was introduced to the beastly conveniences of drip-dry. Roger continued to be manfully cheerful. Briony took me over: mothering me, managing me and breaking my heart with her improvisations, pathetic attempts to make a home out of a cloakroom. It was the gas meter which broke my patience. I do not mind being cheated or charged excessively. But I cannot bear meters especially when I need my coffee and cannot find a coin. This particular gadget, as I told you, was fed on half crowns. It had been so fixed by its rapacious landlord that it took two of these coins to boil a kettle. In a fury I gave a week's notice.

I was at this time seeing a good deal of one friend, who was then living with his wife, in Chelsea. I was seeing them because his wife had shown great interest in my tangle and had offered to mediate by going to see Rose Marie when she could be found. I confided in her openly, as I did with her husband. Returning from one of these sessions to my squalid perch in Cheyne Row one night, I was astounded to see that the house was ringed with press photographers. I scurried off to Boodles and from there telephoned Briony who was besieged. The next morning there was a nasty story about the impending divorce in several newspapers, a particular inside story in the *Daily Mail*. I knew a reporter on that paper and asked him how this copy had come into the paper's possession. He was embarrassed. He advised me to be careful of my friends. Eventually he told me that my friend's wife has sold the story to his paper. From other enquiries I made, I discovered that the *Daily Mirror* had been paying twenty pounds a week to a girl tenant living in the flat below me to alert the paper if ever you came to see me so that they could get a photograph. I decided not to see out the week in Cheyne Row, but to leave immediately.

Again Ben came to the rescue. He offered to take both children off my hands and to take them on a ski-ing holiday to Austria. They went. That's how, you remember, I got back to you, briefly.

Having mislaid my wife, other inconveniences had descended upon me. My bailiff, Cutter, had gone beserk and given me a week's notice just when I couldn't manage the farm myself because I had to be in London to see my solicitors about the divorce. I had my furniture moved to Devonshire. Now in this state of total entropy, emotional chaos and financial mess, I suffered an issue of blood. The sight of this alone nearly killed me with funk. My sister had had cancer of the rectum. I was certain that I had not long to live. This did not please me although my life had become not worth living. I panicked and alerted you to my imminent demise. I raced up and down Harley Street and eventually found the right specialist. After suffering extreme indignities of a rectal examination with the insertion of a camera, I was informed that I had nothing more serious than piles.

'But you should have an operation,' the doctor said, 'before they get any worse. I'll arrange for you to go into King's College Hospital on Friday. I will do the job myself.'

'Is it a serious operation?'

'No. A matter of decoking.'

'Painful?'

'It is rather a sensitive part.'

You alone were sympathetic. I didn't know where Rose Marie was, so I couldn't tell her. But that same day I had lunch with Eliot.

'You'll remember I had the same operation some time ago. It's very painful. They put a cork up your rectum to prevent you from excreting. And when you do. . . I was in the Clinic. . . Very disagreeable experience.'

Possum fell into a reverie of what he had suffered; I became morose at the thought of what I had to undergo. I knew myself to be a physical coward. I would have gone to prison in preference to hospital.

You too were depressed, not only because the operation would part us for a week or two, but because it would prevent my supporting you at the première of your film, *Virgin Island*. How those occasions used to terrify you. Now you would have no escort, nobody to choose your dress, your shoes, or say which handbag to use. . .

The day before I went into hospital, Briony received a short note from Rose Marie. It gave her address, a flat in Weymouth. What a strange place to have one's wife, I thought. My impulse was to go there immediately, but I found I couldn't postpone my operation. The only consolation I had was the thought that, when Briony told her mother that I was in hospital, this alone would alarm her enough to get in touch with me herself. She could hardly ask her solicitors to send me a bunch of flowers, or request Messrs Smellie and Co to report on my condition. I knew she'd be anxious. Or rather I couldn't believe she wouldn't be. She wasn't. I never received a post-card, let alone a flower. After the operation, though my bottom was stitched up with something resembling a bicycle chain and was as uncomfortable as sitting on a circular saw, I found this omission from Rose Marie more difficult to bear. It hurt me; it fretted me; it bewildered me. You saw that when you ran in every day with your load of goodies: half-bottles of champagne, tiny roses and grapes from Jackson's. You knew then that a banana from her would have cheered me up. It wasn't as if I was dying. But how did she know that? I couldn't believe she didn't care.

My temporary obsession with my health prevented me from sharing your success in *Virgin Island*. I read the reviews you heaped on my bed. I pretended to be pleased for you, though I felt that this success would take you from me. But you refused every offer. You never missed a visiting hour.

Uncle Tom had been right to warn me. When they removed the stitches and gave me some laxative to enable my bowels to function again, the pain was unendurable. It was like giving birth to a rugby fifteen each with their boots on. I cried unashamedly. Pain belongs properly to women: at any rate physical pain does. I had not been designed to endure it.

In this extremity, my surgeon visited me. You were in my room. I suppose he thought you were my wife: for he presented you with a metal object which we both mistook for a pepper-pot.

'After he leaves here,' he said, 'you must insert this into his anus once a day to keep it open to prevent the wound healing together.'

The thought made me nearly faint. When the fiend left, you sat there on the end of my bed clutching the pepper-pot in one hand and a tube of ointment in the other.

'He says this stuff spread over the pepper-pot will freeze it and partially anaesthetise the buggery.'

You seemed very happy at the prospect.

I resented this.

'Why does this prospect cheer you up?'

'I feel I'm now necessary to you. If I've to use this on you every day it means I can't possibly go to Hollywood next week.'

'Were you going?'

'I was supposed to. I didn't want to. Now I can't.'

You clutched the pepper-pot proudly like an Oscar.

I had a telephone by my bed; Rose Marie didn't ring. I scattered the post each day looking for a get-well card. It didn't come. I couldn't believe it. I knew Briony would have told her that I'd gone into hospital for an operation. I could not believe that she had not responded. The fact that we were to be divorced seemed to me wholly irrelevant, a mere piece of contemporary morality of no consequence to the true relationship between us. I began to suspect that her wretched lawyers had advised her against coming to visit me. Even so, she could have telephoned or written. Or was Gretchen's presence and influence preventing that? I lay there day and night fretting feverishly. You too could see what was upsetting me.

After about ten days, the house-surgeon said I could go home the next day. To you that meant your flat. You cast yourself as Florence Nightingale and made every preparation to convey me from bed to bed. But what did I do?

Without telling you of my plans I hobbled into my car, feeling faint, wretched and sore. I drove out of London in what I hoped was the direction of Weymouth. I'd thought it was somewhere near Brighton. The wretched place had moved to Dorset. I followed it, sweating from weakness, a little delirious too, the petition in my pocket, wholly irrelevant, legal and trivial, nothing to do with feelings. And as you knew my love for Rose Marie did not, not, mean I did not love you. Thank

69

God you at least were not putting that pistol of either/or to my head again. Was this not because you loved her too?

So I drove on recklessly, dangerously, chain-smoking and missing my way. It was dark when I reached Weymouth. I sought out the flat. I even succeeded in finding it: a dingy boarding-house in an ill-lit street. I parked, staggered out and rang the bell. No answer. I rang again. Could they have seen me or the car? I knocked on the door. The whole house in darkness but no curtains drawn. I had to accept the fact that there was nobody in. I drove to a 'Grand' hotel on the front to telephone in case they'd seen me and were lying doggo. But nobody answered. Though I had had nothing since breakfast and was bleeding badly, I decided not to risk having dinner. Instead I drove back to the flat and sat in the car to wait Rose Marie's return. I assumed she'd gone out to dinner or to a cinema. Before leaving the hotel, I realised suddenly that I'd left the hospital without telling you my intentions, or leaving a message to say where I'd gone. So feeling miserable about all your pathetic preparations to receive the invalid, I telephoned you. You were out too. I visualised you chasing round London searching for me. So I rang my sister in Devon to tell her where I was. She was not surprised. Her advice to me was to sit it out. She promised to let you know somehow where I was.

It was now nine o'clock. By 10.30, I knew Rose Marie couldn't have gone out to dinner. By 11.30, I had to admit she hadn't gone to a cinema either. The house was still in darkness. Where was she? I couldn't think. About 12.30 I returned to the hotel with the certainty that I had a high temperature. There I wrote a note to Rose Marie asking her to ring me at the hotel and went back to put it in her letter box before crawling exhausted, bloody and delirious into bed.

I did not sleep. I *watched* the telephone believing I would see it ring more surely than hear it. And I was frightened she might ring and not wake me.

At 7.30 I drove to the flat again. But I didn't ring or knock this time. For I saw the curtains were now drawn. So Rose Marie was now there. This meant she had ignored my note. Probably, too, she'd been in the house all the time ... I felt the

70

axe on the back of my head. I got into the car and drove back to London, back to you.

You knew where I'd been. You asked no questions. You put me to bed. I slept for twenty-four hours.

You abandoned everything to nurse me. You even administered the pepper-pot every twelve hours, though each time I cursed you as I writhed in pain from it. And you suffered my emotional distress too, yet sensed it was not on your account. The physical discomfort was nothing compared to the mental anguish I was suffering.

Love is not love, which alters, when it alteration finds, I said to myself over and over again trying to forgive her for this hurt. I knew nothing about women. All I knew was I could not have behaved like that to her. Men lack women's ruthlessness. Even so, I could not believe that this hardness was true of Rose Marie.

I confided in my few friends. They told me that it showed that she had made up her mind. They advised me to accept the situation and I was completely unable to do so.

That dreadful winter wore on. I was miserable in myself though happy with you. You had moved into a flat in Dolphin Square. I was part of your luggage, you may remember. We were still very much in love. By which I mean each of us ran home to the other, and telephoned one another throughout the day, anxious when we were parted, vulnerable when together. Yet there was always a shadow. Rose Marie's absence was that shadow. We were both aware of it, though seldom mentioned it. You saw me glance at the post. You noticed my brief disappointment when I answered the telephone. You thought the divorce was distressing me. You did not know that I could not get myself to accept it.

With infinite gentleness you began to take some of Rose Marie's responsibilities. You began collecting suits I'd left at odd cleaners. And though you were little more than a child yourself, you visited Roger at school; you started to mother Briony. The children responded. And when your shooting schedule permitted we used to fly down to Welcombe to keep an eye, or rather a wink, on the farm. You even played hostess there and invited the Harewoods down for a week-end.

I remember I used to be left too much alone. That was because your studio car came to drive you to Pinewood at 6.30 a.m. You had to be made up and on the set by 7.30. Naturally you always woke me. So I had a long day in which to brood.

About this time, I persuaded Roger to get leave from his house-master so that he could slip down to Weymouth to try to persuade his mother towards some reconciliation. He went bravely but hopelessly. When he returned he tried to persuade me to accept the situation. Both he and Briony had. But that didn't impress me. Neither of my children had been married to their mother. . .

I don't think you ever knew of this visit of Roger's. It was not that I was deceitful but that I didn't always tell you things which would hurt you. As I say, or you said, I was a coward. This duplicity eventually led me to hurt you badly, the most painful moment of a painful winter. And what made it worse was you had planned and schemed for that to be a happy Christmas. It was our first alone.

You'd never had the opportunity to organise a family Christmas before. You began to shop for it in the first week in December, sneaking into the flat with enormous parcels which you hid under the bed. Your usual extravagance was cubed: enough food for a battalion of besieged Gurkhas arrived: a Christmas tree that was too tall to stand upright; and stocking presents for Roger and Briony who both let you down by electing to go to Weymouth instead.

Perhaps it was that, or a guilty conscience about the amount of money you'd spent on us, that made you suddenly switch from your film star role into Sister Virginia. But for the next week you abandoned shopping, whenever free from the studio, to organising a group of actors to accompany you to amuse patients in geriatric wards in hospitals in South London. Though I couldn't act, I tagged along and watched you go from bed to bed making the sick laugh and the dying smile. What was it you used to sing in your best cockney?

A lonely little sparrer
Flew all the way to Rome
And on his 'omeward journey
He met a great big 'awk
Who plucked off all its feffers
And said: walk, you bugger, walk.

Yes, you see I remember, though you always said I was never listening.

Even on Christmas Day itself, before you allowed me to give you a present, you assembled your motley troupe at some hideous hospital in Brixton and we traipsed behind you bearing your gifts as you danced into the cancer terminal wards.

It was past two o'clock before we got back to Dolphin Square. You told me to sit and play the gramophone. A fateful mistake. I played Mahler. You said I wasn't to come into the kitchen. Not unreasonably: there wasn't room for two. But I longed to help you. I could cook. No, I'm not being rude. I'd have eaten the linoleum if you'd have served it with floor polish sauce. And about two thirty you announced that dinner was served, sir. You'd dressed for it too. A tiny turkey enough for twelve; cranberry sauce, five vegetables, dozens of balloons, candles burning, and a bottle of champagne in a bucket.

I congratulated you. You said if I didn't stop congratulating you, the turkey would be cold. I carved. But bloody Mahler had unleashed me. Always instantaneously sensitive to my moods, you put your knife and fork down and immediately went to the telephone. You asked for the time of the next train to Weymouth.

I felt ashamed that I hadn't been able to hide the emotions I was feeling.

'Don't feel guilty, it's quite natural for you to want to be where Roger and Briony are on Christmas day. . . There's a train at 3 o'clock. That gives you only twenty minutes. So run and get a taxi.'

I didn't move.

You found my coat. Pushed me to the door. Then you ran back for something.

'Here, open the champagne for me.'

Then you flung your arms round me.

'No. Hurry back. I'll keep the champagne for our supper.'

Of course the moment I'd gone I knew I should have stayed. Typical, for whenever I stayed I found I should have gone. As decisive as a roundabout. Divided . . . It was the longest journey; the slowest journey. The train stopped at every station. On every one I saw you standing there on the platform. I'd hurt you badly. I'd hurt myself badly. We were so close, our wounds were shared.

When I eventually reached Weymouth feeling cold, guilty and miserable, I walked around till I found Rose Marie's new flat. She had moved from the one I'd waited outside so ineffectively after leaving the hospital. Her new residence was a typical sea-side boarding house on the forlorn and deserted front. Sounds of Christmas festivities emerged from some of the houses in the street. Nobody was about: everyone was tucked up with his family. I stood outside Rose Marie's door for some considerable time hesitating to ring, dreading her studied coldness, feeling as welcome as a travelling salesman in cholera germs. But it was Christmas. Surely at this time, when everybody was supposedly celebrating the birth of one who'd preached love, some forgiveness might be found to somebody whose only error was he'd loved too much? But adultery is a different thing, they say. Is it?

I rang the bell with precisely the same feeling of warm anticipation which I used to experience regularly at school when I tapped on the house-master's study door knowing I carried a note which would lead to his caning me. Briony answered the door. She panicked and fled. There was whispering, a hurried consultation. I stood on the draughty step. I could hear the raucous, recorded false laughter coming from a television parlour-game. Always this counterpoint. Eventually Briony reappeared with Roger, both children wearing coats and scarves. They had been given permission to take a brisk walk along the blustering and forlorn front with their errant parent. I perceived that the script had been written by Messrs Arside and Finglestein. It was not proper for the petitioner to say hello to the defendant. Legal etiquette caressed me like sandpaper.

Roger put a brave face on the prospect of a route march into a wind which was embracing us like a glacier; Briony, slightly resentful at having her television programme interrupted. It was too windy to walk. We huddled on a bench on the front, Roger trying to understand my distress.

'Why did you come down?'

'Because I wanted to see Rose Marie.'

'Didn't that mean leaving Virginia?'

'It did.'

'Which one do you love?'

'Both.'

'You can't do that.'

'Why not. Don't you love me and your mother?'

'Yes.'

'Then it is possible to love two people.'

'Your parents. That's different.'

'We think it's different. . .'

I gave up. It was an unfair combat. I didn't want to confuse the children more than they were confused. Briony said little except to ask after you and thank you for the Christmas present you'd sent her. She liked you so much but felt she was betraying Rose Marie by admitting it. Eventually, I told the children to go home to try to persuade Rose Marie to come out for a drink with me before I returned to London. They thought this would work, especially if they could get her alone. They left me sitting on the bench. They told me to give them half an hour and then call at the house again. I waited in the shelter of a hospitable telephone box. It was warmer there.

Then I loped back to the house and eventually rang the bell. Rose Marie appeared. She looked far from glacial, embarrassed perhaps, but clearly pleased to see me though trying not to show it.

'I thought you might come out for a drink?'

I could see she wanted to but the edicts of Messrs Arside and Finglebum rang in her head.

Gretchen now appeared briskly to reinforce her. Or was she the script writer? Then, in front of me began to bully Rose Marie. She was most foolishly rude to me. It was Gretchen who closed the door on me. At this interview she won the

75

game but lost the match. Because it was then that I resolved that I would have to rescue Rose Marie from this liaison.

I stood looking at the closed door for a few minutes then realised I had no alternative but to return to London. I knew there was a train in ten minutes and ran breathlessly to the station in time to see it leave without me. A beery porter told me that 'there isn't another train, it being Christmas day, you know— for another two hours.' I waited on the platform. I was coughing badly. I felt hungry. You had, I remember, refused to let me have any breakfast because that would spoil my appetite for the luncheon I had abandoned. My family had not been hospitable. I had eaten nothing all day except two packets of *Corporal.* Even the chocolate slot machines on that dreadful station were empty.

I was the only passenger on the train. No corridor. No buffet. A stop at every gas–lit station at which nobody got in, and nobody got out. Was I travelling or was I dreaming? This journey was one of the nightmares I have lived. I think I fear death because I believe it will be like that journey. Slow, unending, going in the wrong direction. The penalty for pulling the communication cord was only £5. But what then? It is, perhaps, better to travel when you've nowhere to be.

It was long past midnight when I let myself into your flat. I tip-toed in. Then I saw that your Christmas dinner had not been cleared away, nor had you eaten. The bird like a great gaunt ship on the table; the decorations looking incongruous; the champagne still unopened. I went into you. You were not asleep. You had been crying. I told you what happened in Weymouth.

'Poor Rose Marie,' you'd said, 'poor you, poor us.'

Then you'd hauled me into bed. I was too tired to eat, too miserable to make love. Our one and only Christmas. Long live Messrs Finklestein and Arsehole; bless the purveyors of conventional morality.

Even after visiting Weymouth and writing to Rose Marie I did not receive a reply so I wrote to her again. I am not an inarticulate person. I begged her to meet me at mid-day at the

76

Vega Restaurant in Leicester Square. It was there that we had first met twenty years before.

I have never been late for an appointment. It is not that I am polite, but anxious. For this particular appointment, I arrived half an hour early because I was frightened that I might be late; and, if I had she might not have waited. That was silly of me, for Rose Marie was seldom punctual. I had said I would meet her at 12.30, so I arrived at mid-day. I did not enter the restaurant, but stood on the kerb opposite so that I could see her arrive from any direction, and perhaps pay her cab.

Standing there, hoping she would come, I feared what you would think if you knew of this meeting. I hadn't told you. Why? Because, I repeat, I am a moral coward. Of course you knew I was divided. You did not know how much divided. I did not know that either. I was soon to discover.

By 12.25, I found I was getting cold feet, fearing that my meeting with Rose Marie might lead to a break from you.

When she had not arrived by 12.45, I felt relief; or thought I did. But yet I did not move away. But after another half hour of watching each taxi, and every woman entering the restaurant opposite, my relief had revealed itself as despair. Did this mean that Rose Marie had ignored my invitation? That we would never meet again? I could not face that thought. Those who can be separated, never loved. Those who can be divorced were always separate. Or so I thought. I still do.

So I stood immobile, a gale blowing through my mind, emotional chaos, the consequence of trying to drive myself to choose between Rose Marie and you. I knew that this was false to feeling, or at any rate, to mine. But I tried. I tried to be conventional and tidy. And when Rose Marie had not arrived at 1.30, I pretended that that meant I could now be undivided and be with you as you were with me. But less than five minutes later I was suffering something like grief because she had not come at all. And for another hour I persisted and waited, and endured swinging on a pendulum which was pivoted in my own insecurity. Swaying between the two of you, terrified of losing either. All men are babies; but I am such a baby, I don't need one mother, but two.

It was not until three o'clock that I allowed myself to walk away from the restaurant. Even then I began to excuse her. Perhaps she had never got my invitation? Possibly I'd put the wrong date, the wrong restaurant? Perhaps I'd asked her to dinner, not luncheon? Should I go back to the restaurant to see if there was a telephone message for me? After all, if her train had been derailed or she'd missed it from Weymouth she might have telephoned.

She hadn't. Women are more ruthless than men.

Even when you were still playing in *The Catalyst*, you had confused me by your frequent reference to 'Mother'. Sometimes you would speak of her with deep affection, sometimes with scant respect. I couldn't understand how your attitude to her varied so considerably, sometimes within the same day. I must have known you for a month or more before I suddenly realised that you had two mothers: Phyllis; and the Mother Superior of your convent at Newhall, whom you adored. Clearly, after your parent's marriage broke up, you had blamed Phyllis for abandoning you to your grandmother and had then transferred all the affection you had had for her to the nun. It was not a difficult process. I soon discovered that the emotion had been reciprocated. I saw from the Reverend Mother's letters to you which you proudly showed me that she, and other nuns at Newhall, too, did not look upon you simply as an old girl but, in some special respect, their favourite daughter. Though Rose Marie and Briony too had been to a convent, I had never run into the special relationship which always existed between you and that place.

When we started to live together you constantly urged me to go with you to Newhall to meet Mother. I wasn't enthusiastic. We were living 'in sin'. I didn't want to be put on the mat. I feared their influence on you might be to take you from me. So I prevaricated. Then, a few days later, you disappeared to Newhall yourself, and returned radiant because you had told Mother all about us and she had approved, and had said how much she admired my work. 'Do you know,' you went on, 'she asked me if I could possibly use my influence over you to get you to sign her copy of *Our Lady's Tumbler*?' To prove your point you produced the book. I wrote an inscription.

You made me promise to accompany you to Newhall the next time you went. That was soon. You were frightened I'd change my mind. Had I a mind?

As we drove down, I couldn't help noticing your excitement. You were not going back to school, you were going home. I couldn't understand this. That had not been my experience at school. The spacious building impressed me. You ran up the steps taking me by the hand. You gripped it as we entered the Mother Superior's study. Was this to give me courage or to make our relationship visually evident? It was the latter. You were completely unashamed. Your Mother hardly glanced at me, she was so entranced at the sight of you. You were certainly at least a daughter to her. Then she turned to me and read me like a book. She must have missed out a page or two because she showed no sign of disapproval, put me at ease and offered me a whisky. She was in control of herself and the situation. She could bat better than I could bowl. We talked for a few minutes about the theatre but only so that it could lead to you. Within a few minutes she was showing me photos of you in the last play you had done there. She gave me copies of photographs I admired. After this she asked me if I would like to see the chapel.

I found myself standing before a larger than life wooden statue of you posed as the Virgin Mary. With you beside me in your red velvet shirt, black stockings and high heeled shoes, I felt ill-cast as the immaculate conception.

A year or so later, when writing *Abelard and Heloise* for you, I remembered this statue:

I could show you the wall round the garden
    we have built from the stones which came from the stables;
I could take you into our chapel
    where we have a new statue of Our Lady
carved out of one piece of oak!
    (the model was a street urchin,
a girl with a mouth of cherries
    and a flower of innocence in her eyes)

Your Mother gave me a photograph of this statue too. I never asked you to sign it.

I gathered from one of the sisters that you had at one time wished to become a nun at Newhall. That you had become a film-star instead didn't distress them. They knew the strength of your attachment. They could wait. I, like your work, was only a temporary distraction of which they could afford to approve.

What was it we had in common? Why did we cling to each other though the world tried, and eventually succeeded, in parting us? I suppose I am known as an intellectual; in my more idiotic moments I mistake myself for one, too. But nobody, especially yourself, could have made that error. You could never have passed an 'A' level; most subjects including Greek were Greek to you. You'd been educated at a convent and knew your way blindfolded through the Missal but thought a square root was a vegetable. So what did we chatter about so incessantly? It wasn't the theatre or what I was writing, or rather was supposed to be writing, though poetry was something you had an innate feeling for and an uncanny competence at writing yourself. Nor were we always talking about the emotional tangle we were in, though we did discuss Rose Marie more than each other. Did we gossip about our friends? We were too obsessed with each other. Tell me. I'm listening. Honestly, I can't remember. 'Knickers,' you say.
'I beg your pardon . . . ?'
Yes, now I remember . . . So much of our time was spent discussing the virtues of our respective inventions. We had this eccentricity in common. I had always had an invention up my capacious sleeve ranging either from one as stupid as the waterproof cover, worked on the principle of a venetian blind, to cover a bicycle seat to prevent it getting wet when not sat on, to the more ambitious submersible chain of rubber pontoons to carry oil beneath the waves and to be drawn by a tug to avoid surface weather and the high cost of tankers. But your inventions seemed more urgent, especially that idea of paper disposable knickers which girls could burn instead of washing. I must admit I couldn't fault the idea. Our fortune was made: until we began to hawk it. But I must tell you you were right: there are several factories now manufacturing them. A pity

you didn't get a royalty. Another of your inventions was eventually taken up. I remember persuading a director of a well known cosmetic firm to meet us for luncheon while you explained the advantages of a lipstick which could be applied by a small brush. He couldn't see the advantages. Odd, that his firm marketed it within three years. And there were others, though I was teasing you when I told somebody you'd invented a Thermos-flask hot water bottle.

But our inventions couldn't have amused us on those weekends which we often spent cuddled up like waifs squatting in a sodden ditch. These ditches were scattered over half a dozen counties. We took shelter in them because we were banished: I had no flat of my own in London and before your mother moved to Germany, you had no place either. So we lived like gypsies without a caravan. In the boot of my car you kept a frying pan, a kettle, two plates, one knife, one fork and a cake of soap. This was our gear. Then we'd set off for nowhere and arrive late after the shops were shut. Or, on expeditions which were properly prepared, we would reach some lane which led nowhere, and there I would be sent off to find twigs and bits of gate pales with which to attempt to light a fire, while you burrowed in the boot of the car for the steak which you'd misplaced, or the frying pan you'd forgotten. But generally I managed to get the sap to sizzle or smoke. Then lacking the frying pan, you'd lay the steak on the unblushing embers. Though the entrecôte never cooked, it was slightly smoked. There's nothing so delicious as *Steak Tartare à la Fumée* especially when served with a lettuce you'd snatched out of somebody's garden. And the ditches were always damp because it was invariably raining; we would abandon the struggle of erecting the tent and doss down in the back of the car.

These were our happiest moments: when we were playing at mothers and fathers or cowboys and indians, wholly unconscious of enacting a fantasy, completely absorbed in a reality we'd created with two twigs and half an onion. I can remember loving you, hating you, leaving you, returning to you, but can't recall once being bored by you. It wasn't sex which made us so much of one another— though neither of us had any complaints; nor, as I say, did intellectual interests bind us: it was, I think, your ability to play games seriously which made me so obsessed by you. I treasure that intent expression you had when you announced that 'dinner is served' in our ditch. Whatever you did, you did it seriously, even if that was playing hide-and-seek; if you cooked, you always cooked badly; when you once made a dress you used glue to do up the hem. It wasn't what you did that mattered, but your innocence, your vulnerability that continuously broke my broken heart. Some people said at the time I'd become infatuated with a film-star. They were wholly wrong. That part of you was the one game you couldn't play seriously: it was tedious to us both, a masquerade and a sham which made you feel ashamed. It was the child, the urchin in you I adored. And you liked me because only with me could you be the *gamine* that you were.

Only once did I catch you being insincere. There had been a party on the stage of the Royal Court Theatre. Before it, you had said you shared my views about George Devine. But at that party, I had observed you making up to him like any tuppenny actress. I called you a hypocrite and, using Tom Eliot's favourite word, 'a trimmer'. You wept from shame. This incident not only drove you to confession, but back to Newhall for a retreat. I didn't mean to be so censorious or severe. God knows, in my time I'd trimmed enough to that tribe of inflated pygmies that inhabit the jungle of Sloane Square and Shaftesbury Avenue.

And one of the invisible diamonds I wear on my paws, is the memory that while you were away at your convent, Briony volunteered to come round to Dolphin Square to tidy up your flat as a surprise for you when you returned. She was responding to you as a person, not to an ethic which was dead. She was a Cavalier then, not a Roundhead.

Her task was not easy. You were the untidiest girl I ever met: toffee papers on your dressing table, a chaos of odd shoes on a chair, a nest of handbags in one corner, contracts stuffed into a raincoat pocket, a pile of unopened letters on the floor.

And of course our joint invention of 'The Green Cross' didn't help to keep you tidy. That itself gave birth to a mountain of paper as those projects always do. I can't remember exactly how 'The Green Cross' came into existence. I have a vague recollection that I had written an article for Beaverbrook about how few hardwood trees were being planted in England as opposed to the plantations of soft coniferous trees. I recall ferreting out the statistic that only forty-five walnut trees had been planted in England the previous year; and had suggested in the article that the *Daily Express* should sponsor an annual 'Tree Planting Day' on which everybody should plant at least one sapling, those who hadn't land of their own to be permitted to plant on the grass verges of the roads. You thought this a brilliant idea. Unhappily the newspaper never took it up. So we perversely and inevitably decided to go it alone, to found a society to get this Annual Tree Planting Day established. Remembering the many months I'd wasted sitting on crumb-fingering committees of abortive societies, I hesitated. But you pointed out how effective Marion had been in founding the Leeds Piano Competition; and that I, too, had managed to get the Royal Court off the ground out of my own pocket. So, I agreed. The next step was to give this brawling brat a name. I suggested 'The Green Cross'. You were delighted. That same day you ordered thousands of green cross badges to be made in enamel which our non-existent members could wear on their lapels or as brooches. Quires of headed writing-paper arrived. We registered ourselves as a charity though we were the only donors. Then, as usual, I went off on my begging expeditions wearing a dinner suit.

As usual, George coughed up first. Next my sister. Then, of course, Elaine Blond who sent a cheque large enough to put us in business. I wrote a pamphlet or a leaflet. We bullied those we knew, and pestered those we didn't. A few, a very few, responded: and these sent a guinea: they thought that was effort enough. Nobody planted a single sapling — except myself who had five acres of Marsland valley planted with the help of the Forestry Commission. But they insisted on Sitka. It's called Virginia Wood. Perhaps this paragraph explains my present routine: I write this stuff in the morning, and then plant a couple of trees in the afternoon. All hardwoods. I hadn't seen why I was doing that till now.

On one of my dreary and weekly visits to Messrs Gilderstein and Bash, I was asked to list my assets, since these would have to be shown to the Court in order that alimony (which in my youth I had thought was an aperitif) could be properly assessed. I did this; my solicitor then warned me that since I had two children at school, several homes to maintain, farm wages to pay and apparently no liquid assets (perhaps it was an aperitif), I would be wise to take my financial position seriously and give my mind to it. This advice led me to make several disastrous decisions from which I have not yet recovered though they were all effected fifteen years ago. I remember that you advised me not to do anything. Naturally, as you didn't even know what an overdraft was, and never even filled in the counterfoils on your cheque books, I ignored your opinion. A pity. I would be a rich man now if I had listened to your feather-brained fancies; instead I consulted such specialists at Messrs Sothebys, Scrimgeour, and Knight, Frank and Lightly.

My first move in Operation Harbouring My Resources was to fill a taxi with my small collection of drawings from Orme Lane. About twenty Gaudier Brezkas, several of which had been given to me by Pound, Epsteins, Rodins and Cocteau drawings: I took these along to the Bond Street flea-market. I think they must have been sold in Ascot week. The prices I received scarcely covered the cost of the framing. Several Gaudiers went for under £20. I assumed the Epsteins had been given away with the catalogue. This idiotic gesture of retrenchment netted me seven hundred pounds. I would have preferred sending them to my friends as Christmas cards. Today the proceeds from any two of these pictures would keep me for almost a year.

My next, or simultaneous move towards financial probity, was to sell some land. I was prompted to do this because the weekly column I had written in the *Evening Standard* for fourteen years called *Jan's Journal* had been terminated. It had kept me in bread, if not butter, which was what Beaverbrook had intended. But Max Aitken lacked his father's quirks. Malcolm Muggeridge, hearing of my financial difficulties, immediately offered me a column in *Punch*. I accepted; but even so, I had to sell several farms. The largest of them, a place called Bowden, I owned jointly with my sister. She always made the mistake of taking my advice in matters I knew nothing about on the principle that two heads could not possibly be worse than one. This particular farm had been taken over by the Royal Navy during the war. The fields had been used for target practice. Great craters pock-marked the best meadows. The fences were down. None of it had been cultivated for five years. The farmhouse was in ruins: ratings had even burned the lavatory seats and doors in the winter for firewood. Our only income from its two hundred acres was from the few thousand pounds the Admiralty had paid us in compensation — so we decided to sell rather than find money to fill in the craters to rebuild the house: it seemed a sound decision. I think we received forty pounds per acre. The purchaser, knowing more than we did about local planning and development prospects, resold it within three years for £250,000. That's what I like about Town and Country Planning, it so often develops the planners.

My next piece of shrewdness was to sell Leddon Farm which adjoined my own place at Welcombe; I thought I also needed some capital then to help finance the Royal Court Theatre. Leddon had a sitting tenant. I sold for four thousand pounds. I pass the place every day. Its present value is eighty thousand.

Yet at that time neither of us gave these figures a thought. We were right. Money is not important. If we think it is, it is because it is we who are unimportant.

What drives me to write this? To keep my promise to you? God knows, I broke enough of them in my time, or rather yours. Exhibitionism? A need to parade our love to those who lack it themselves? Few men have pursued privacy as I have done, living as I do, in the most isolated place left in England, my nearest neighbour a mile away, my nearest friend now on the other side of the Atlantic. The need to justify my behaviour? I am too arrogant for that. And of what use is justice anyhow? Mercy alone is what I need, and for remorse there is no mercy. I suppose I write because it is the only thing I

85

can do: it is my only way to you. Those who can be parted never loved. If only our love had died. It would have been so easy to kill it.

I now became morbidly fascinated by anybody I met who had been divorced or was about to be. I wished to learn whether they too suffered from my indecision and resistance to being tidied up, filed and put away. But the more I questioned them, the less affinity I found. Without exception I discovered that none had any regrets: they found the procedure a bore, that was all. But none suffered from my ambivalence, duality or indecision. They'd fallen in love with Joan, so how could they possibly still be in love with Jane? Dumbfounded, quaking at their emotional simplicity, I stared at this phenomenon as if it was a new planet which had just heaved into orbit.

Determined to rescue Rose Marie from Gretchen, I eventually decided that though I could not persuade her to return to me, I might succeed in getting her to live with Briony. Dimly I realised that the best way of effecting this was to make the arrangements, then face Rose Marie, not with an appeal but with a *fait accompli*. Women respond to practical alternatives, not their reason, not your emotion. Accordingly I rented Father Patrick McLaughlin's flat in St John's Wood, then told Briony to inform her mother that these arrangements had been made. Rose Marie accepted gratefully. I had at least extricated her from Weymouth. Even Gretchen found it difficult to argue against a lease. She too returned to London to live with another of her girlfriends.

You were delighted when the Weymouth menage collapsed. The fact that this made Rose Marie more accessible to me didn't alarm you. You, too, were pleased to see her rescued from Gretchen. How you hated her. I didn't then ask myself, or you, why you disliked her so violently. But I do ask now. Was it fear of her? Or was it jealousy? I don't know. I don't believe you knew either. Or if you did, you ran from the truth; perhaps that's why I found it so hard to know where you were, since you hid from me and from yourself.

But, I remember, soon after Rose Marie moved into McLaughin's flat with Briony, you came home to Dolphin

Square one evening from the studio and ran in with your eyes blazing with anger.

'That bitch is here spying on us,' you cried. 'Gretchen is down there working at the petrol pumps.' You went to the window and pointed down to the garage.

Knowing how irrational you were where she was concerned I thought you had imagined it. I said so. That made you very angry. I went down to look myself. You were right. There was Gretchen in white overalls filling a car not twenty yards from the entrance to your flat.

'At least, they won't need to employ Messrs Smellie and Co. any more,' I said.

A year's resentment becomes a solid thing, a stone under the foot of the mind. Consequently it was a relief to discover the reason why Rose Marie had not sent me even a cauliflower when I had been in hospital, for my painful and humiliating operation the previous autumn. To my astonishment I discovered from her that, at that time, she had been informed by her solicitors that I had put the police on to her mother and had accused the old lady of theft.

We couldn't think of a germ of validity to this story until I remembered the expensive camera you had brought down to Welcombe, which had meant so little to you that you'd forgotten you had ever owned it. We noticed one day that the useless camera was no longer hanging behind the door. Because of the insurance, we had to inform the police.

A couple of bobbies came out from Bideford to complete the routine. I told them that we didn't suspect anybody in particular. They thought it likely that a casual hiker had seen it through the window when the cottage was empty while we were down on the beach or out riding and had nipped in and helped himself. But before the police left they had asked me if we'd had any guests recently. I had said none then glanced at the visitors' book and noticed that Rose Marie's mother, who was over seventy, and a resident in an old people's home at Torrington, had been out to stay at Mead for a few days. I had not seen them take a note of her address which was apparently in the book.

The dolts had then continued their idiotic routine enquiries. Their very appearance had of course frightened the old lady. And when she discovered the nature of their enquiries she concluded that I had, by instructing them, suspected her. She was justifiably indignant. As she saw it, she had been accused of theft by her son-in-law and humiliated by these enquiries in front of the other ladies in the Home. The drums had beaten. Lying on my bed-pan I had not heard them, however. It was a relief to me to know there was some reason why I didn't get even a card.

But my life could have been squashed like a cockroach under this flat-footed, clumsy move. I daresay there were others which I never discovered.

After Rose Marie left Weymouth, she shared Father Patrick's flat alone with Briony then moved to another which she discovered had been where Katherine Mansfield had lived. It was in Acacia Road, St Johns Wood. She seemed happier there, she began to paint again. I visited her frequently. To our relief we found our friendship undiminished in spite of our joint efforts to bust our relationship. But like ferrets her solicitors still pursued me, and the petition was, as they say, still on the table. Rose Marie persisted in wanting a divorce. I didn't; I knew that between us it could only be paper . . .

Then one day I had a call from my people, Messrs Gilderstein and Bash. They pointed out that the action, which at that time I'd been advised to defend, was going to prove most embarrassing since Rose Marie's people had not only named you, but Antonia too. The fact that there was no justification for her inclusion was of no consequence. I realised that I now had to persuade Rose Marie to drop this farce which I didn't want anyhow. It occurred to me too that by including Antonia she knew that the action couldn't proceed. Therefore, I instructed my gang to explore the possibilities of a Separation. This was eventually agreed and I formed a small trust for her out of which she purchased a flat, 117D, Hamilton Terrace, to provide a home for herself, Roger and Briony. She seemed relieved too and immediately began happily to make curtains with one hand, and to decorate with the other. She was immensely competent and economical too. Though I was still living with you, these moves of reconciliation, or of quenching the flame of the law, disturbed you. Our future became obscure whenever you looked at the law and not at our feelings.

Your girlfriends began waving red lights in front of your eyes and smacking their lips, pleased at the prospect of our relationship foundering since they had not achieved one of its qualities themselves. And if I behaved with some ambivalence, you did too. No sooner was Rose Marie in her flat than you were sending little presents round — like this glass ashtray now before me, or rushing round still dressed as a Hussar when you got a lunch break from a television show you were rehearsing in an empty school in St John's Wood.

During the winter of 1959, you had motored North to open some cinema in York and to do some television up there. I took the opportunity to dart down to Welcombe. You wrote to me.

Arab mine,
 To combat the sadness at least — stillness. Already I feel quiet in your breathing and the mercy of your being . . .

Just as your poems had surprised me, phrases in your letters pulled me up too. You were only twenty-one; you'd never passed an exam; what right had you to invent phrases like *the mercy of your being*? You were supposed to be an empty-headed film-star. I didn't know who you were. And these pages fail to discover it. But I stole the phrase. If friends are not worth stealing from, they're not worth knowing.

With you at Dolphin Square, and Rose Marie now settled in her flat at Hamilton Terrace with Briony, I spent my time hurrying between you, a man with his coat tails flying. But in my case, the tails were the back doors of my car which failed to stay shut and were a considerable menace to all but myself. I generally drove using only one hand with which to steer and the other to change my tie or links so that I would arrive properly dressed before you or Rose Marie, that is, wearing

89

the appropriate emblem either had given me. Though I do not forget that I had one tie which both had bought me jointly in Bideford.

Neither of you knew how often I visited the other. Though, of course, Rose Marie knew I shared your flat. And because divorce proceedings were filed I was not supposed to be seeing either of you: Rose Marie because of the Proctor; you, because I did not wish you named. So like a character in a French farce, I had to pretend I wasn't anywhere. Indeed I became furtive, a fugitive in flight from myself. When returning to your flat in Dolphin Square I used to choose a different entrance every evening. I remember each one was named after a renowned naval hero. One of these was Duncan. And I would use the Duncan lift to reach you in Nelson, pausing to check my tie before rushing in to greet you if you happened to be back from the studio.

In this frantic fashion I ferried myself across London three times a day. A ping-pong ball: two girls playing table tennis. My bounce getting less and less, no time to get the car doors mended in spite of George's warning, driving recklessly, fearful of being late, always arriving early. A nuclear particle propelled between two magnets held, if not contained, within a field.

But you will remember how once I did arrive late. I had left Rose Marie at about ten o'clock in order to get 'home' to you by 10.30 when you said you'd be back from the studio. I was tearing down Kensington Church Street when an elderly woman suddenly walked off the pavement to cross the road. I braked hard and swerved. I thought that I had just managed to avoid hitting her. But when I looked, she'd disappeared. I got out of the car and found her lying on her face on the road about three yards ahead of my car. Could I have hit her and she'd bounced off that distance? I turned her over. She looked undamaged but very drunk, a broken bottle of gin still in her hand. I drove my car to the kerb. Then I went back to get the woman to her feet. She thanked me and apologised for falling over in front of my car. She was, she told me, very drunk and would be most grateful if I would see her home. I removed the broken glass from the road and took the remnants of the bottle from her hand. I supposed she wanted a lift. But she said she lived in an adjoining street and produced a card bearing an address which she admitted she carried because she was frequently in her present condition. She was a woman of about fifty; well spoken, possibly a school mistress.

I supported her up the street and heaved her up the stairs to her flat on the third floor. The door was opened by her husband, an amiable Colonel-type in felt slippers. He had black coffee ready waiting. From the casual way he thanked me for seeing his wife home, I gathered this was part of their routine. He offered me some coffee too, and while his wife was out of the room, he told me that she was a very well known writer of children's stories who always got blind drunk when she'd completed a new one.

That evening I was very late. You were in bed and pouting. I told you my story. You didn't believe a word of it. The next morning I tried it on Rose Marie; she didn't believe me either. You had much too much in common. I do not mean me.

One of my happiest memories, and there are many, so many, was when you marched into the flat in Dolphin Square when your mother had said you could take it over since she was going to Germany. You looked contemptuously at her double bed. 'This won't do,' you said. 'That will have to go.' You set off immediately for Harrods.

'We want to buy the largest double bed you have in stock,' you announced unashamedly to the staid assistant as if threatening immediate consummation. Then you turned to me. 'And we'll share it, and the bill.'

The bed arrived. We had omitted to take the precaution of measuring the room. The men only just managed to get it in. They had to crawl over it to get out of the room. 'At any rate we shan't be able to kick each other out,' you said. 'Let's christen it.'

I spent almost a year shuttling in this fashion between your and Rose Marie's flats. I had written nothing very much but a few short poems. The four-handed play I had started a year ago had got lost amongst the make-up on your dressing table.

One act was written, the rest was fading from my mind. I couldn't find the willpower to complete it and anyhow lacked any place where I could be alone to write. I was going through one of those periods which any writer experiences when he tells himself he will start next Monday and then, when that day arrives, finds a reason which is a transparent excuse. I felt guilty but guilt had become a second skin to me. Then suddenly both you and Rose Marie decided to take me in hand, you resolved that I should go off alone to finish the play saying I was not to return until I had finished it. You packed my suitcase. Feeling like a schoolboy, I drove to Hamilton Terrace to tell Rose Marie that I was off. She congratulated me on a resolution which was not mine. I wished her good-bye then drove off down the road glancing behind me to make sure I had remembered my suitcase and unfinished manuscripts. Both were there. I had forgotten nothing; but I suddenly realised that I had completely failed to acquire a destination. I stopped the car somewhere in St John's Wood to decide where to go. I could think of nowhere I wished to go if I was to be alone.

To be without a destination is to have a momentary foretaste of death. Sitting in that car, not knowing whether to go north, south, east or west I became acutely conscious that my identity itself was precarious. Who was I but where I belonged? Who was I but where I was going? Who was I but to whom I was travelling? It's a brave man who sets off to be alone. I was a coward. I already felt homesick, but I was not sure if I had a home.

Eventually, after sitting there watching the amorous windscreen wipers failing to embrace, I picked up the A.A. handbook from the dash board, and opened it, not to find a way, but to be given a destination. Arundel was the town listed at the top of a page. So I drove there.

It looked like any other town: the same shops in the stereotyped High Street. There is only one town in England now: a self service bore.

From habit I took a double room in what is known as a comfortable, three-star hotel, a castrated bordello, where a bible bound in red lay on the bedside table, and there was a minute piece of white soap in a contraceptive covering. These are not rooms but cells, where loneliness drips from the walls, silence screams from the ceiling, where the mean gas fire has a lascivious meter. I flung the manuscript of Act One of my unfinished play on to the tabernacle of chastity and went out to buy a large note book in which to write the final act. I had no idea how to finish the play. I returned to the terrible room to read Act One. I had almost forgotten what it was about. Reading it I was most unimpressed. It did not seem worthy of completion. This was a way out. I telephoned you to tell you. You were adamant: 'I won't see you unless you come back with the finished play,' you said. It was a Friday evening. I felt cornered, condemned to authorship, sentenced to a stretch in an Arundel Tourist House. My depression became panic. Some fools think it must be a privilege to be a poet: I would prefer to be born a fishmonger. I sat in front of a blank page. My impulse was to turn the bloody thing into a one act play and to kill off the four characters in a single *coup de théâtre*. But the buggers wouldn't lie down. How wonderful it must be to be a creative artist, idiots often tell me. The dolts don't realise that it's enough to bear, or forbear, oneself; it is too much to have to carry these imagined characters and their situations and unhappinesses, too.

I realised I could not stand the loneliness of this room for more than a few days without going off my head. I took myself for a walk into Arundel Castle park. 'An act has thirty-six pages,' I said to myself. 'If I write twelve a day, I could leave by Tuesday.' This seemed hopeful. All I needed was a synopsis for Act Two. I took myself out to one of those dreadful steak bars where vegetables are served on oval platters whether you want them or not, where prawn cocktails are *de rigeur* and Irish coffee is urged and ghastly musak pisses incessantly over all. On the back of the menu I sketched a synopsis. For the next three days, I lay on that bed and as the walls closed in upon me, scribbled my twelve pages a day, loathing each word, merely writing to escape from my predicament. On Tuesday, I drove back to you. You asked for proof that I'd completed the play. I handed it to you. You sat and read it. 'What inspired you to write like this?' you asked, embracing me.

'The terror of an unopened bible,' I said. 'That, and the unfriendliness of a piece of plastic-covered soap.'

The BBC asked me to change the title from *Playback* to *The Rehearsal* when they televised this piece. The critics praised it. At least I know where their destination is.

For some weeks I had been complaining of toothache. You called me a baby. Then, when you saw I was not feigning, you urged me to visit your new dentist, a Pole in Wimpole Street. Not trusting my courage, you made the appointment and drove me to the door.

He was a young man, good-looking, with an air of competence. He looked at my tender front tooth in my upper jaw. I told him that I did not wish to have it extracted unless absolutely necessary. He decided to X-ray the tooth and my upper gums. When this was done, he gave me an appointment for the following day. Again, you dropped me in Wimpole Street.

I sat myself down in his chair while the man shuffled through the negatives. Then he came and faced me.

'These X-rays indicate that you have a growth in the roof of your mouth,' he said.

'A growth?'

'I'm afraid there's no doubt about it.'

I felt faint. Faint from terror. A growth meant cancer. My greatest dread. So many of my relatives had died from cancer. But that did not endear me to this disease. I stood up and glared at the negatives. The man indicated some smudge on it.

'No doubt about it,' he repeated.

So this was it. It had seemed a normal morning. And here I was right up against it. Cancer of the roof of the mouth. I felt cheated; I had had to summon up courage to go to a dentist. I had expected no more than a stopping. What right had this man to inflict me with such grave news? I thought I was condemned to death, and not quite early enough to be of any literary interest.

I left the dentist standing and bolted straight to my doctor in Chester Street. I told him that a dentist had just informed me that I had a growth in the roof of my mouth. He took this news with more restraint than I thought decent.

'We'd better get you into the Middlesex,' he said. 'I'll have a word with Allen. He's the best throat and nose surgeon in the Country.'

'Spare no expense. This lot is probably on the Chancellor.'

The doctor hadn't followed.

'The more I spend, the less my death duties.'

'I see what you mean. But you mustn't be so morbid. Mr Allen will probably be able to cope.

'Probably?'

He nodded.

'Be brutally frank.'

'That is impossible until they open you up.'

'Have you experience of a case like this?'

'Only last month.'

'And?'

'The operation was successful. The man has a false roof and is now learning to speak again.'

'Christ,' I said, and felt sick again.

The doctor made a couple of telephone calls.

'Everything's fixed,' he said. 'They're expecting you in a private room tomorrow morning. Allen will operate the following afternoon. I will of course be there, too.'

I didn't hear anything else he said because there was a muffled funeral bell tolling in my head. I left his surgery, hailed a taxi as if it were a hearse. I didn't feel sad just angry and indignant. I felt I had been cheated, deprived of my life even before I could waste it all. But though I didn't feel sad, I felt fear: not of the unknown, but of the known.

'*Hooves of bullocks will tread upon my eyeballs,*' I said, badly misquoting Yeats.

I felt sick again. I had automatically directed the taxi to Dolphin Square. I realised you wouldn't be in. I had to be comforted and consoled instantly. I needed a brandy; I had to draft a will. In a turmoil, I re-directed the taxi to Hamilton Terrace. Rose Marie would probably be at her flat. She would be sympathetic; the frivolity of our divorce and our differences would fall away instantly. Maybe you and she would be drawn together. Though we'd failed to find a *modus vivendi*, there seemed more likelihood now that a *modus moriendi* might

95

emerge. This thought was of some consolation to me as I bounded up those outside iron stairs to her flat.

Rose Marie was surprised to see me and wasn't sure what her attitude to me should be. So, taken off her guard, she was natural and friendly. She saw I was in a state. Over coffee I gave her my news.

All antipathy and reserve immediately dissolved. She was appalled and as frightened for herself as she was for me.

She asked me to stay to lunch and started worrying about whether to buy me any pyjamas to take into hospital. She was at her best: practical and wholly concerned for me. I was confirmed in my suspicions or hopes that her true feelings for me were undisturbed in spite of the lawyers divisive efforts.

The grave is the only place from which to see our lives in true perspective, I thought.

'I shall be at your bedside when you come round from the operation,' she said, taking my hand to hold on to something herself.

After this reconciliation I felt more cheerful, but aware that death was a high price to pay for making life bearable. I left her flat and spent the next hour in a telephone box trying in vain to contact you. But you weren't at the studio. I had four hours or more to wait. So I decided to go to see Stephen Rawle.

He too was appalled at my news and didn't disguise the fact that medically he thought it very serious.

'At the best, you'll have difficulty with speech,' he said.

'At the best?'

'I think I'll ring Rose Marie and see her,' he said. 'She'll be needing to talk to somebody.' That was thoughtful of him — at five guineas an hour.

After I left Rawle, I telephoned Birchams intending to scribble a codicil to my will so that you had a small bequest. But the bloke who dealt with my affairs was out hunting . . . that's the way we're disinherited.

When you did eventually return to Dolphin Square, it was late. Waiting for you was almost as painful as the news I had to give you — you arrived in the gayest of moods. Even a day's shooting had not depressed you as it usually did. You saw I was looking sorry for myself and immediately began to tease me for being a baby because I had been to the dentist. When I told you his diagnosis you didn't believe me. I told you that I had seen my doctor — who was now also yours — that I had been to see Rose Marie who had been sympathetic, and had had a session with Stephen Rawle. You immediately telephoned all three, not because you doubted my story but wanted support. Then you too worried about my lack of pyjamas. Perhaps tactlessly I told you Rose Marie was seeing to them. You frowned as though deprived, then smiled and rushed off in your car returning with a new blue dressing gown — which was subsequently stolen from my car outside Boodles — and a pair of otter-skin slippers which I'm wearing as I write this. You then tried to alter your shooting schedule and failed. You said you'd be at the hospital as soon as the operation was over. I refrained from telling you that Rose Marie would also be there. Somehow I knew that if the worst — as I liked to think of it — happened, you two would be appropriate ornaments to my death bed and would be of considerable consolation to each other. Indeed this picture of you two whom I loved and whom I knew loved each other overcoming convention made the sacrifice of my life seem not wholly in vain, or meaningless.

Lost in these maudlin thoughts, I didn't notice that you were doing something extremely odd. You were tidying the sitting-room and moving all your things from the bedroom all into it.

'I shall put you in the bedroom to convalesce,' you said, and: 'Your nurse will sleep in here, otherwise you'll never get better.'

Like a child you were playing at being a nurse. Only a red cross on your dress was lacking. Part of you had always wanted to be a nun, part a nurse. And there were other parts. But that evening you were happy in your new role. I had to remind you that I had not had the operation yet and there was no reason why I shouldn't take you out to supper.

It was not an easy meal: you knew I was frightened to death of death. The thought of it alone was likely to kill me. You too had had several relatives die of cancer. But you were a good actress and your performance that evening should have won you an Oscar: you mimicked to make me laugh; you asked me questions to which you really knew the answer to make me feel intellectually superior. And when we returned to your flat you continued the game of being my nurse, insisting you were my night nurse too.

As usual the studio car called for you at 6.30 a.m. You were shooting at Pinewood. You'd left my breakfast on a tray (only coffee: a note said no food before operation — Nurse's Orders), my suitcase ready packed.

My room at the hospital was comfortable. By my bed a bouquet of miniature red roses from you. How had you managed that? Rose Marie admired them as she put her carnations beside them. Then she helped me into a pair of pyjamas though I had no disabilities beyond chronic funk.

I made certain that my cigarettes would be within reach when and if I came round. 'If I didn't want a cigarette then I would know I was dead,' I said. Then Rose Marie left; she said she would come back later. She whispered to the nurses. Came back and kissed me. I was touched. My impulse was to drag her into bed but for once I overcame it. Then Allen came in and shook me briskly by the hand. My doctor hovered. An anaesthetist did his stuff and I tried to count your roses. But I wasn't reconciled. Like Marlowe, I died cursing.

An hour or so later, I regained what we vainly call consciousness. I saw your red roses and continued counting them. I felt Rose Marie's hand in mine. My tongue told me I had no front teeth. The loss of these did not console me for being alive. Perhaps vanity is what life is. Now my tongue began to explore upwards. To my surprise my tongue met an impediment: it was the roof of my mouth and it seemed intact. I began to spit blood. Rose Marie held a metal basin. She had, I could see, been crying. I treasure her tears: pearls I wear.

Then this deathbed scene was rudely interrupted by two nurses. One carried a tea tray; the other went to the wardrobe to take out my clothes.

Rose Marie asked why she was doing this.

'I presume Mr Duncan will want to dress before he goes after his cup of tea,' she said with the minimum respect for her patient. Then both left the room.

Rose Marie and I were too astounded to speak. Allen entered.

'How are you feeling,' he asked without undue concern.

Rose Marie was on her feet. 'The nurses have told my husband that he can dress and leave,' she said incredulously.

'Why, doesn't he want to?'

'Is that usual after an operation for cancer?'

'For what?'

Now he looked bewildered.

'Your husband had a slight abscess at the root of one tooth. I don't know why I was called in to do a job any dentist could have done. But there it is — and my account too.'

He left the room. My doctor entered. He confirmed the diagnosis. There had been no trace of a growth, merely a minute abscess, but while I was out a couple more came out as well, which would have had to go in a year or two anyway. Mr De Vere would have my dentures ready by Thursday.

Somewhat embarrassed, he too left the room.

'Get dressed,' Rose Marie said curtly.

I did as I was told, even missing my tea.

Her mood had changed. I wished I was still under the anaesthetic.

'I suppose you'd better come to Hamilton Terrace,' she said bundling me into a taxi, 'since you're still spitting blood; I'll have to mop it up since your girl friend is not around to do so.'

Still feeling doped, bewildered and toothless, Rose Marie put me to bed making a few pointed remarks about her brave husband who had had to go into a private room at a major hospital and employ the country's best mouth surgeon merely to have three rotten teeth extracted. 'And,' she reminded me, 'I had mine done on the National Health.' She was bitter, very bitter.

'I thought I'd got cancer,' I said honestly.

'You don't fool me, merely a filthy trick to frighten me and everybody else to get sympathy. A mean and despicable trick.'

Rose Marie was angry. Not unjustifiably angry. My explanation went unheard, certainly not believed.

Just then you telephoned. Without any teeth I couldn't speak to you myself. The conversation between you and Rose

Marie was brief. You had gone to the hospital, discovered the corpse had flown and concluded that he had apparently preferred his wife's nursing to your own in spite of the preparations you'd made. You were hurt, justifiably hurt. Three teeth missing, two angry women on my hands. I began to wish I had died.

But within twenty-four hours, I was out of bed, dressed, and fidgeting to get my dentures. I felt that a brick had been thrown through the plate glass window of my face. I was at a considerable disadvantage. I couldn't even articulate my explanation of the events. Rose Marie maintained, not without some apparent justification, that the whole scare had been a put-up job.

'You thought that by pretending to have cancer I'd stop sueing you for divorce?'

I repeated that the Polish dentist had X-rayed me and had said I had a growth on the roof of my mouth.

She was still not convinced. The situation between us was now glacial. And still you sulked, too. You had every right to be angry. I noticed that you had made up a bed for yourself in the tiny sitting room. While in your bedroom you had made pathetic preparations to receive the invalid who had apparently preferred the wife who was divorcing him to the mistress who had obviously spent half a night — since in those days those were the only hours which were yours — tidying our chaos, buying new sheets, and even putting grapes and flowers beside the bed.

It was the sight of Pedro, the black panda which I'd bought you, waiting on the pillow for me to cuddle in your absence since you'd put yourself in the next room, which broke me . . .

'Now I suppose you'd like some coffee before you go back to Hamilton Terrace?' you said going into the kitchen. 'Your nurse will be worried where you are. Or didn't you tell her where you were going?'

I stood watching you grind the coffee; you looked sad, too defeated to complain. Without looking at your eyes I knew there were tears in them. You were weeping too, I knew, not for yourself but for us.

I pulled the plug out of the kettle.

'No, don't touch me,' you said. 'I don't want that.'

I put the plug back in the kettle.

'But you can undo that zip if you like and I'll run and dress up for you.' You were all smiles again. Mischief. You ran out of the room. I could hear a parcel being ravished as only your impatience could deal with inanimate things.

You couldn't find any scissors. From the smell I knew you were burning the string.

The kettle boiled. I made the coffee, waited. Then you tip-toed in dressed partially like a nun, partially like a nurse. A costume from the studio. You looked so serious whenever you played games.

'I'm sorry the invalid let you down,' I said moving Pedro over.

'I shan't take you to my convent again if nuns' costumes have this effect on you.'

Then afterwards it was you who wanted me to dress. 'You must, poor Rose Marie may be worried, probably she's expecting you for dinner. You mustn't disappoint her, too.'

That was typical of you. I was never sure where I was, or where I should be. Divided utterly.

'No,' I said. 'She's so certain my cancer scare was a put up job that she says she never wants to see me again.'

'No?'

'No.'

It was too late to argue. And of course the studio car would be calling at six. We had to get some sleep, or as much as we could get.

A few days after my cancer scare, we decided to part for ever again. Or rather you did: I could never decide anything in life knowing that death was so decisive. We hadn't quarrelled. You simply convinced yourself that it was better for the world if we died to each other. I think it was your parents' divorce which haunted you. You didn't want to be the cause of another. That, and your affection for Rose Marie. And I suppose you saw that I myself would never let her go. Since I couldn't or wouldn't choose between you, you did it for me. Or tried.

You decided to go to some friends in Suffolk. I said I would return to Devonshire. I tried to reconcile myself to letting you fly away. While you packed in the bedroom I scribbled this thinking of your 'lonely little sparrer' song and left it on your sitting room table.

How fragile this frightened sparrow is
　　Which I clasp in my hands;
If I clutch it to keep it,
　　I will crush its wings;
But if I release my hold
　　It will fly away

So fly away, fly away!
　　Let my love be your little wings:
I cannot, will not, hold you
　　Knowing that where you go, I am.

I will be the air that bears you up;
I will be the branch you rest upon;
Your flight from me, shall be to me:
　　Where you go, I am.

Oh fly away, my love, fly away!
Look! my hand is open, only my eyes are closed. . .
Adieu, my love, adieu.

What miracle is this? Its fear has gone.
Now it makes its nest within my fingers.
The cage is no more; it is a home.

But the resolution to release you didn't last for more than a few hours as this letter I wrote to you that evening shows.

I love you. That's the only way I can start this letter. It's the only thing I feel this morning. I phoned you only an hour ago. But I can't work, I sit here looking at your *Catalyst* photo — at your drawing, at your panda, at your rosary hanging by the fire place. I am not any more in my self: I am in you. Oh, please *be*, please stay just as you are and change where and when you want to. I swear I'll be there. If you become a whore, I'll become a pimp; if you become a bus, I'll become a road: if you become old, I'll be your age. You ask me (Why?): If we stopped being lovers would you love me still? The answer is: I will always love you. There is no way out, no alternative: *for what I love, I become.* Sweetheart, be secure; know that I love *you*, not just the doll of you, the tease of you, the vamp of you, the minx of you. But why did you ask that question? Tell me. Are you frightened as I am? Sometimes frightened? We are married in our eyes; don't let this neon world blind you to that. If we move gently, gently as grass grows, as milk yields, as birds build, we shall get there. Maybe we've nowhere to go? Maybe all is in the going? Sweetheart, hold my hand: it is I who am the weaker. It is I who can't swim straight, it is I who need your wisdom. Don't mistake that. True I have knowledge but that's nothing but the collection of cigarette cards and old programmes.

But I am worried, I am not very secure either — not because of you but because I want so much more of you than life seems to want to give me.

I drove down from London yesterday — but I didn't look at the lovely country. All I seemed to be seeing was you standing in your dressing-room singing your little songs just before I left. I swear that was when my heart finally broke into bits of you.

What are we to do? If anything takes me from you, I shan't want my life anymore. I could live without the you I undress; I could even live without the you who sleeps in my arms; I could *perhaps* manage to survive without your insteps, your slim thighs, your smooth back and the apples of your breasts: but I know I can't live without the joyous innocence of you, the pouting urchin in you, the ingenuous generous child of you. I am not usually profane, but I know that you have something very pure in you; it is holy and it is the little saint in you I need. Oh don't fool me and tell me you sin . . . Your 'sins' make my saint. It'll take me years to make you understand — to make me understand. Intuition is immediate. I recognise. Oh if only I could explain. I can't. I can't. And now I am crying I don't know why. I only know writing these lines on this page has made me weep ... I will go and make some coffee. Oh if only I could explain. There is some secret, I know, if only I could explain. And it is so simple. Christ it is so simple. Perhaps that's why I can't do anything to explain it. Perhaps it all is as the grass is. But know this, my love, you have what I looked for and when I am said to be dead tell them I am looking out of your eyes.

Let us be exceptional. Genius is the capacity to break *their* rules and make *its* rules. What do I mean? I mean there is nothing love cannot do or create. We are separated. Are we? Take this page of paper now. Sit down, there. Shut the door. Be alone. Now close your eyes and look at me. My hand is your hand. Touch your breast. Enjoy being in your body. It is I who am loving you. It is you who are loving me. We are becoming; we are only. Oh flow to me.

That ring, our ring: promise to wear it forever. Whatever the world seems to do to us. I don't know what will happen to us. I do know I love you. I know I can trust my love. I know I can trust yours.

Rose Marie is making moves back to me. I have told her that whatever the future holds you are part of it for me. She says she accepts that. Can you?????? You say: Nail me to your cross and let me bleed for you. I will, if I can kiss your wounds, if you can be my scars. Oh, my love, don't abandon me or loose me or us. For of my love for you, there shall be no finish of.

Now I shall mooch around and fill in the day somehow till you phone this evening.

Bless the telephone. Bless Faraday
                    Marconi
                    Bell
                    Edison
        Blast Henry Sherek
                    Gretchen
                    Trains to Newcastle
                    Newcastle

Trains to Edinburgh
Edinburgh.

I enclose some pocket money. Do you want any more? It's all I have on my desk.

Yes teach me to waltz please. With you, it won't take me long. Please do that.

At this moment, I am entirely possessed by you, as much as a child in your womb. I promise to lie there quietly in your little belly and I won't kick or make you sick. But sing to me occasionally.

Arab

But no letter came to me from you. I wasn't surprised. I knew you to be the stronger. What I didn't know was that you wrote more often than I did. The only difference was you didn't post your letters. I found them by your bed when I rushed round to you hearing from Rose Marie that you were unwell. So much for that parting. But we had tried, hadn't we?

During the war, the Admiralty had asked my permission to erect a small look-out hut on the cliff edge above West Mill. It overlooked the approach to the Bristol Channel. On a still summer evening in 1940 I had stood on that spot to watch eight ships in convoy blow up and sink within fifteen minutes. The hut the Admiralty erected was made of galvanised iron on a concrete base and measured ten by six feet.

After the war, the Admiralty offered to take the hut away or let me have it as a gift. Since it was rusting and unsightly, I asked them to remove it. This they did.

A few years later, I found myself repeatedly going up the cliff path to sit for hours on this site. The view attracted me because it contained no sign of humanity: the open Atlantic, the bracken and gorse covered cliffs, giant boulders on the beach beneath. The only signs of life were the buzzards and a single unmated falcon. I was drawn to this view which had not changed since the Cambrian era. I became interested in geology of which I knew nothing.

One day, when you found me squatting out there on those concrete foundations, you asked me why I didn't build myself a gazebo there? It was a brilliant idea which had never occurred to me.

I immediately applied for planning permission, getting an architect to draw up a simple design of local stone. I waited six months or more, and eventually the application was refused. I appealed. A tribunal was held in Bideford. The press had given the matter considerable publicity. My argument weighed with the judge who, very much to the annoyance of the local borough surveyor, allowed my appeal.

We started to build the next day. Roger volunteered to get the stone down to the site and himself erected a hauser and block and tackle. I ordered a large plate-glass window to front the hut sufficiently strong to stand Atlantic gales. You came down that week-end; and since the hut had been your idea, insisted on laying the foundation stone under which you put a lock of your hair folded between two half crowns. Bill Pengilly, my invaluable Man Friday, and Tom Wade were both masons. It was slow work because sand, water, and cement had to be carried by hand part of the way down the cliff to the site. However that summer, putting in odd hours in between the harvest they managed to get the walls up about three feet.

Then suddenly, very much to my surprise and consternation, I received an order from the local surveyor 'to discontinue all building because I had exceeded the licence which was to build only on the existing foundations'. But this we had not done. A casual glance would reveal that. But he maintained his objection; refused to meet me or my architect on the site; and warned me that if I continued to build, he would have the building demolished. This piece of bureaucratic spite was more than I could tolerate. I instructed my solicitors to report the matter to the Home Secretary and to request another tribunal.

Eventually this was convened in Bideford. Since I had not exceeded the licence and had built on the existing foundations, my solicitors and I were wholly confident that our appeal would be allowed. My architect produced photographs to the court showing the Admiralty concrete blocks clearly beneath the stone walls; my solicitor demanded that the Inspector should himself go out to see the building. But in spite of

106

acceding to this request, he turned down the evidence of his own eyes and announced that he would advise that my appeal should be disallowed. It appeared I had been routed. My lawyers were astonished. I had already spent £600 on these tribunals.

My defeat was a matter of some jubilation in the Press. . . 'Poet's hut turned down' etc. It must have been these reports which prompted the Home Secretary to reject the decision of his own Inspector and personally to send me a telegram: 'I don't see why you shouldn't have your gazebo.' My gratitude and delight was of a pyrotechnic order. Building recommenced.

I write this in that hut, on the desk made out of the Captain's teak door off the *Green Ranger* which was wrecked that winter on the cliffs beneath. Few things have ended so happily for me. This hut has been a refuge. A snail needs a shell.

Throughout this period I swung as a pendulum: when I was with Rose Marie, I was thinking of you sitting alone, waiting for me; when I was with you, I was, as you often saw, worrying about her, telephoning her, telling you I was talking to my agents or publishers; lying, not because I wanted to deceive, but because I did not wish to hurt you.

When Rose Marie left me, none of my friends really understood my dilemma. Nor did my psychiatrist. To them, my problem was simple: I had to make a choice. To this simplification I replied that it is not natural for a man to say whether he wants his right leg or his left amputated when he needs both. This invariably shocked them. They all based their advice and reasoning upon the fallacious and conventional assumption that a man cannot love two women at one and the same time. They couldn't see that I did. Somehow they'd managed to assume that our local morality, a mere western convention, was an absolute, like Newton's law of dynamics. I often used to think of old Asraf, Prince Victor's valet, whom I'd known as a child. I had seen that he had been devoted to each of his four wives. Oddly enough, he was never arrested for bigamy, though English Law doesn't exempt Mohammedans off the Edgware Road where he resided.

Is that why you always called me Arab? Or was it, more likely, because of my colouring? When you didn't use that nickname you called me "iggins'. You saw yourself as the urchin from the Goldhawk Road, where you'd been brought up by your grandmother after your parents had separated, and I was the professor in *Pygmalion* who used to cover up your gaffes at dinner parties when you talked of Puccini's *Otello* or Verdi's *Dream of Gerontius*. I never knew why you used to call my whispered corrections 'Operation Bathmat'. With George, any girl's musical knowledge might have felt some strain. What you never understood was that my friends loved you for these gaffes — just as Ezra Pound had warmed to Rose Marie when she'd congratulated him on *The Winding Stair*; or I had felt endeared to the Mayor of Leeds for the trouble he'd taken to be able to quote from my play *The Ascent of F6* when he was introduced to me.

Sometimes these pressures of convention, applied by my friends, or the sheer exhaustion of rushing from you to Rose Marie then back to you again, drove me to the point when I was about to make a choice between the two of you.

I decided to go home to Devonshire to think the matter out. I made up my mind to be alone for a few days then have my psychiatrist join me at the farm. Of course, even before I got on the train at Paddington, I had realised that this decision would entail giving you up. I realised that if we broke, you were young enough to recover, whereas there were twenty-five good reasons why I could not leave Rose Marie: we'd been together twenty-five years. In a moment of rare honesty the night before, I'd prepared you by saying that my love for Rose Marie and my concern for her would inevitably be a shadow between us. You had guessed that I was going to say something like that. It hadn't prevented you packing my bag or ironing my shirts. Damn you for those little things which always undid me, made my resolution melt. So, by the time the train had got to Reading I was sure I was going in the wrong direction — away from you. At Westbury I got out of the train to return to London and to you. Three minutes later, as I watched the train disappear, the pendulum swung again: I resolved to telephone you, say a final good-bye to you, then ring Rose Marie to tell her to meet me at Paddington and to ask her to fly with me to Madrid.

I might have done this if the telephone box had been empty. It wasn't. A woman was having an endless gossip. I waited, keeping my hands deep in my pocket lest I should open the door of the kiosk to strangle her. I had made a decision. It was urgent that I implement it instantly. I waited. I tapped on the door. Nothing could stem the babble. I walked away. My resolution walked off too. I now found myself on Westbury station not knowing whether I wanted to go back to London or on to Devonshire. I allowed trains to each destination to pass me while I sat there transfixed with indecision.

Nobody has really suffered unless they've endured this kind of paralysis. I was at Westbury. I had no reason to be at Westbury. But I didn't know in which direction to go. That wasn't because I really didn't know what it was I wanted. In my transparent heart: I did. I wanted you both. To have my cake and eat it. What's wrong with that? Doesn't every child want that? And ain't we all nothing more, I mean less, than children?

But since I saw that I couldn't have you both— though how happy we'd often been when the three of us had been together — I decided, as I always do, to act against myself and to proceed to Devon, to be a martyr without either of you. I eventually boarded a train for Exeter and took a taxi from there to Welcombe.

It didn't help that ten minutes after I had entered the fireless and ghost-filled house you rang because you were so worried that I hadn't answered the telephone before. It didn't help that ten minutes after your call, Rose Marie rang to ask how things were at home. And it didn't help me choose between you when she told me she was just off to meet you as you were going to a film together. This was so typical of her: to confuse me utterly.

Impulsively, and sickened by the sad house, I tried immediately to order another taxi to get me back to Exeter. But before I could effect this, Tom Eastwood drove into the farm yard. He had driven down in pursuit because he had just received a commission from the Edinburgh Festival to write a

Song Cycle for guitar and tenor, Julian Bream and Gerald English. This is a form I love: anything remotely associated with Schubert excites me. Within twenty-four hours we'd agreed on the theme and the number of songs. I wrote three of the poems the next day and promised to post him the other six within a week. Not surprisingly I told him they would be love poems, but love poems of anger. I tried to explain that I wanted to exploit the negative side of this over-trodden theme. Two snippets came to my mind as illustration.

> Why do you hate me so?
> I can't recall doing you any good.

and

> What crime have I committed
> That I should deserve
>   the punishment of your love?

Eastwood left after a couple of days. But I couldn't accompany him because I'd invited Rawle for the weekend. And being in a desperate psychic muddle I needed him to talk to. As I've said, I never discovered what his qualifications were other than his ability to listen sympathetically. He had a gentle manner and considerable intuitive understanding. He described himself as eclectic, rather than of any particular school, but clearly derived most of his ideas from Jung rather than from Freud: and would occasionally veer off and irritate me with Jungian references to synchronism and other mystic bogs. I suppose I kept in with these not inexpensive sessions because I needed somebody to talk to and, having exhausted my friends, had consequently to pay somebody to listen to my 'fore bemoaning moan'. Rawle was particularly useful, being morally unshockable. His tolerance towards me, of course, derived from his own need of tolerance. From where can tolerance or compassion for other's failings come but from the experience of our own temptations to which we ourselves have succumbed? Oscar Wilde and Delacroix would have understood me, Milton and Eliot never . . . Paradoxically I say that if I have any virtue it is because I've 'sinned'. Doesn't virtue derive from *vir*, being a man? How could Christ have become man *if only in part*, without a man's appetites and passion?

With this thought I decided to write a libretto for a cantata on the theme of Jesus and his relationship with Mary Magdalene. I remembered the lines I'd turned up in the *Apocrypha*, sitting in Gerald Brenan's garden at Churriana years before while writing a libretto for Ben on *St Peter*.

> Do not cling to me thus
> While I am yet a man.

This cantata on Jesus and Mary Magdalene was eventually set by Alan Rideout and performed at St Albans Cathedral. It was never published.

Patrick McLaughin had been a friend of mine ever since he'd directed 'Ora Pro Nobis' in 1947. McLaughin was a born actor, but too intelligent to become one, and had consequently become an Anglican priest, whose principal concern was to get plays put on in his church, St Thomas's in Regent Street. Father Patrick was also priest of St Anne's in Dean Street, Soho. The church had been entirely destroyed in the war, but an adjoining building belonging to the church still stood intact.

One day Father Patrick asked me if I could think of any use to which this building could be put, considering its situation in the heart of Soho, excluding that of a brothel. I pondered the matter for a moment and then, unhappily, had an idea. For years, I had missed the old Café Royal — it had been a place where one could go and be sure to meet a few friends and sit there unmolested for an entire evening, spending no more than a few shillings on beer or coffee. It occurred to me that a similar café where artists and writers could congregate would be worth having. Father Patrick was enthusiastic.

I had often toyed with the possibility of having a restaurant. Once Ben, George and I had seriously considered opening a fish restaurant at Aldeburgh: luckily this project had come to nothing.

The St Anne's idea was doomed to be fulfilled. You were

largely responsible; you were as excited by the scheme as Father Patrick. We formed a limited company and I think I found some £1,500; Patrick borrowed a similar sum and you put in another £1,000. Within a few weeks, the decorators had moved in; you wrote round to well known artists asking them to let you have a picture to hang in this new Café Royal. Epstein, Topolski and Piper immediately responded to your blandishments. Ben gave you the manuscript of the Kyrie of his mass. Pound sent you a poem. Tom Eliot agreed to come to the opening.

But he must have forgotten. Everybody must have forgotten. I think only you, George, Patrick and myself attended the opening party. It was a Chaplinesque evening. And you'd worked so hard, forgetting no detail except publicity; pulling your finger out, but failing to pull any strings. The restaurant, which looked so pretty with its red velvet upholstery and its distinguished manuscripts, its two pictures on the wall, its immaculate chef in his white hat, was an instant white elephant. The bills appalled us: even you looked frightened. As if to pour oil on the blaze, we decided to entertain our friends lavishly there, believing the larger our bills were at these meals, the less the deficit would be at the end of the week. This idiocy ranked with Treasury finance.

But I remember one occasion when you and I sat at separate tables, each with our known guest who could be relied upon for their appetite and thirst. I sat in one corner feasting George on jugged hare and burgundy, while you entertained some film tycoon at another table. All the others were empty. I shall never forget that luncheon, because during it, George looked across the restaurant to where you sat, then turned to me and said, gravely: 'You're making a big mistake: Virginia adores you, but if you don't marry her, she'll leave you.' I didn't believe him. I didn't want to. Colds, not advice, are all we take from friends.

In the thirties, I had seen a film called *The Blue Angel* in which Marlene Dietrich played the part of a dancer in a circus. A staid, middle-aged university professor, played by Emil Jannings, fell in love with her. Like Faust searching for Margaret, the professor abandoned his books and university to follow the circus. He was given humiliating jobs to do. The dancer kept him on a string. Eventually the professor became a clown, too, and wore an enormous white paper collar, a red nose, a tiny hat, and baggy trousers. But in spite of the ridiculousness of his appearance, his dignity remained intact because of the transparent genuineness of his affection. By the end of the film, this noble character had been reduced to a buffoon. Obsessed with the girl, he would peep out through his steel-rimmed glasses through which he espied her flirting deliberately with another man, in his presence, as if he were invisible or his feelings did not count. At this moment the last shred of dignity was reft from him; stretching his scraggy neck high above his gigantic collar, the professor mouthed words he dared not articulate, then finally crowed like a castrated cock. The pain and the cruel pathos of this image made a deep impression on me when I saw this film. I now found myself often recalling it as, having abandoned my writing, I traipsed around, following you from film-set to theatre dressing-room, sitting alone for hours while you were on the set or on the stage. I used to sit idly toying with your make-up, sometimes making myself useful by running out to do errands for other actors, such as getting them cigarettes, a newspaper or a cup of tea, trying to be accepted as part of the troupe: an exile from myself.

You remember that midnight charity matinée of the Hundred Stars at the London Palladium? You had been persuaded or bullied by Laurence Olivier to be one of six Tiller girls to his Fred Astaire act. A chorus of film-stars all to be dressed in black, wide-meshed stockings and can-can panties. You had said you couldn't dance. He had insisted that it didn't matter since you had pretty legs. You were terrified. We'd been out to buy the stockings together. Somehow you thought that by involving me, this act would give you confidence and make it feel like less of a vulgar piece of exhibitionism. So I tagged along; you even persuaded me to come to your dressing-room which you shared with the other girls, then stand in the wings while you did your act. The difference was that it was not I who felt a clown on these occasions but you, who loathed flinging your sex appeal across the footlights. You resented it. You behaved like a nun forced to do strip-tease. You were a prude in public, a bawd in private. That's how it should be. And though you always carried a rosary with you, there was one occasion, wasn't there, when you used it, but not for prayer. Having wrapped it round, you couldn't get it off. . . .

During this summer of 1960, you went on tour in a play. I didn't like it and you were unhappy in your part. You persuaded me to come up to Leeds. It was there, squatting alone in your dressing-room, that I wrote this *Solitude* and left it on your make-up tray.

As thrush, lark and linnet are
    So do my eyes rise,
Sing for the life in you
    Joyful at your being. Oh
                be there

Where I am going, when I return to
    Be bark to my ivy
Tree to my climbing
    Be merciful
                be here

Where my hope is, be there where my home was,
    Else I am lost, lonely as driftwood;
Be to the restless river, me
    Clear pool of no purpose
                be still

Peaceful as grass is, grow gently,
    Secretly beneath
Impetuous rain of me
    Be brave at my cruelty
                believe

In my gentleness; forgive me for this,
    Forgive me for that. Contain my disparities;
Accept my extremities. Oh love me wholly, so
    Holy shall you
                become.

You must have liked this poem for you typed it in your tent and gave me a copy. That tent. Always a tent. Nomads. George wouldn't hear of my putting up at a hotel in Leeds and had insisted I stayed at Harewood. But because his mother, the Princess Royal, was in residence, we couldn't smuggle you into the house too. So you put your tent up in the park behind the tennis court. When the tent collapsed about you like a shroud during the following night, you moved the next day to the Harewood Arms at the end of the drive. It is a long drive. I would never have made a Troubadour.

When you went on to play in Dublin, I sensed you were going through some crisis. I didn't know what it was.

Why do I disclose our precious intimacy and privacy? I write only for you, for us. I will censor nothing. Ronald Duncan lived here. I am ashamed not of my life, only of my death. Having written my own life honestly, no grubbing journalist or assiduous PhD will dare to invent what I've already exposed. When the fox hangs himself he is at least saved from the hounds. To meet you from Dublin I got up at 4 a.m. and drove to London Airport. You stepped from the plane holding your present for me in two hands like a child: a paper bag of Dublin Bay prawns. I began devouring them on the tarmac. As I drove you to London I sensed there was something wrong: some strange distance between us, emphasised by your insistence on holding my hand while I drove. Were you clinging to me or to a self you'd lost?

I was unhappily to discover the answer a few days later during a session with Rawle who had seen you the previous day. He blurted out to me, almost as an aside, that you had been unfaithful to me and slept with one of the actors in Dublin. He thought I knew — I had not known. The damage was done. There was a long pause in which I tried to haul myself together, a self which had exploded then disintegrated before my eyes. 'How do you feel?' he asked. 'Bloody angry,' I replied. 'Then you should act out that emotion,' he said, 'so that Virginia can relate to it.'

After he'd left, you returned with some shopping. You were going to cook. It was to be quite an occasion. I'd already taken alka seltza. You stood there and asked me why I was looking

115

so miserable. I fenced. You insisted. Finally I asked you if it was true you'd slept with a bloke in Dublin.

'Yes,' you screamed. 'It's your fault you should have come to protect me.'

'From yourself?' I said going up to you and smacking you hard across the face.

I had never been violent before or since. I was more shocked than you were. You merely burst into tears and ran upstairs and got into bed fully dressed.

'You've given me a black eye,' you said proudly as I sat on the end of your bed.

Then you started to explain how you'd run into an actor's room after suffering from a nightmare and he'd hauled you into bed. A letter you had sent me had given a different version. But I didn't want to hear the details. I left the cottage and walked without any sense of where I was going.

I found myself at the edge of the Round Pond in Kensington Gardens. Elderly children were playing with their trim craft and adjusting neat rigging. The pond looked calm compared to the gale within my mind. Then gazing into the water I noticed a large dead fish floating some distance from where I stood. I waded in to pick it up. The dead fish had suddenly acquired some special or symbolic significance to me. The nautical gentlemen eyed me most suspiciously. It was a large carp and had clearly been dead some days. But now I carried it as though it were a prize salmon. I walked with my burden as far as the Albert Hall when I suddenly became acutely disgusted and nauseated with it. Where does one put a dead carp outside the Albert Hall? In a letter box? I could find no sign of a litter bin. Then, as if inspired, I carried it into the road and placed it in the track of an oncoming bus. The driver probably thought he was seeing things, then he swerved to avoid it. It was only when I saw a taxi drive over the carp and squash it that I realised my purpose had been to drag it from the water and bring it to you and place it on your bed as a strange bouquet to signify what I felt had happened to us too.

But I wandered back to Carmel Court without any spiteful emblem. You were sitting up in bed hugging Pedro, nursing

116

your black eye. I told you about the fish; you didn't believe me; nor did I.

I decided to spend that night at Boodles. It was an expensive gesture. Behaving in a conventional and ridiculous fashion I piled all my clothes into the back of my car. Since I had not put them into a suitcase, I found I couldn't bother to take them out of the car. I never lock a car, for two reasons, firstly I could never find the right key and anyhow I believe car thieves carry a set of them. The next morning, all my clothes had been stolen. I returned the following day with only my tooth brush between my legs.

We were soon reconciled; due, not to my capacity to forgive, but to forget . . . When so much happens, yesterday's bruises seem to fade beneath today's scars. But I can remember how proud you were of the black eye which I was so ashamed about. You went about all that week showing it off as if I had given you an emerald bracelet. 'Look what Ronnie's given me,' you boasted.

To celebrate this brawl, or rather our bruised reconciliation, you insisted that we should give each other plain gold eternity rings. We went to a shop at the bottom of Church Street: to my suspicious eye the rings you chose looked dangerously like wedding rings. When I received mine, I saw it was inscribed 'Arab. Our love for ever. Urchin.' On the one I gave you, I'd written: *Quia amore langueo.* I wonder what happened to yours? I'm sure you wore it till you got a proper wedding ring instead. As to mine, I treasured it, but cursed it: having to wear it when I was with you, then remembering to remove it, like the links and the tie, before I went to see Rose Marie. It was due to this quick change act that I eventually lost it. I searched for days, then realised I was wasting my time anyhow: though I could lose your ring, you weren't so easily mislaid. But I often wonder in whose drawer, on whose finger, that ring rests: gold doesn't dissolve. Somebody has it somewhere. May it bring them better luck than it brought me.

Soon after this, your play opened in London. It was a flop. You were delighted. This meant we could fly off to Devon. It was July. We decided to motor and you prepared a picnic which I agreed to, needing to economize. We stopped to eat it

117

on Salisbury Plain: the whole lot from Jackson's, everything in aspic, the most expensive meal I ever ate.

Perhaps it was this gesture which made me make a few remarks about your double standards: how you were essentially an urchin who'd acquired occasional film-star tastes which did not suit you. And a day or so later when we were riding you told me you'd been sent a film script which so disgusted you that you were thinking of turning in your contract. I didn't take you seriously. You looked cross. 'If you tear your contract up,' I said, 'what will you do for money? You'll have to stop shopping at Jackson's and buying a pair of shoes every day.' At this you scowled angrily. You reined Lucretia up. Dismounted. Then you took a wad of £5 notes out of the hip pocket of your jeans. You tore each one in half. I said nothing: then you took the wad of paper and made a hole in the mud by that gate which stands on the right between Strawberry Water Farm and Watergate. I watched you bury the money and stamp the mud over it. Then you grinned and we rode on. There must have been £100. It's a pity paper is less immutable than gold . . .

When we returned to London from Devon, you went to Bristol to do a television play. Half my time was wasted on attending endless committee meetings for the Strasbourg Festival of the Arts for which Father Patrick had persuaded me to act as unpaid artistic director. I must have drunk a thousand cups of coffee in aid of this non-event. I also had the Royal Court in my lap when I was not darting off to be with Rose Marie.

When your television was over — and how you loathed doing television plays— you insisted that you took me off for a holiday.

'Where?'

'A surprise.'

'Where?'

'To the Rose Revived.'

I thought this would prove to be the name of another of your tents. But it was an old pub by the river about six miles outside Oxford. Unlike our stay in Henley after visiting Piper, when you had reverted to your nun *persona* and kept me at an

118

uncomfortable distance, at this prettily named pub, you became Manon squared.

Even when we drove off to see Professor Henri Fluchère who'd translated my and Eliot's plays into French, you insisted that we stopped to make love in the car while still on a main road. 'A case of decent exposure,' you said as an approaching headlight dipped precipitantly as it reflected from your bottom.

Around this time we really were both nearly arrested for indecent exposure. I had promised to take you, Lavinia and Briony up to Aldeburgh for a performance of *Lucretia* which was being given at the Jubilee Hall as part of the Festival. You three girls insisted I wore a black tie and made arrangements to dress appropriately. You were all in Carmel Court and about to go off to change when I noticed that the time of the performance was one hour earlier than I had thought. So I bundled the three of you into the car, each clutching your rags in your hands.

'You'll have to change at Ben's,' I said.

But the traffic delayed us. At Norwich it was clear that you'd all have to change in the car. With much giggling, the three of you began to strip off while I drove along glancing occasionally to admire the scenery. It was then that a couple of policemen got in my way. There'd been an accident ahead. One of the policemen glanced in the car to observe three girls each wearing nothing but a bra and panties.

'Do you always drive in this fashion,' he asked me taking out his note book.

'One of these ladies is my daughter,' I said huffily.

He looked profoundly shocked.

'That makes it even worse,' he said.

It was, of course, Lavinia who got us out of this scrape, I can't remember how.

Janet Kidd is my oldest friend. We had been seventeen together. She is Beaverbrook's daughter. We had met in 1936, canvassing for Sir Ernest Petter in the St George's division, when he had been defeated by Duff-Cooper. Then Janet had had a couple of unhappy marriages, one to the Duke of Argyll;

119

finally she had married a Canadian and settled in Somerset where she farmed extensively. She kept a large number of show-jumpers and a Hanoverian stallion to which I sometimes sent a mare. We met fairly regularly at the Horse of the Year Show. But sometimes she would call on me to help her out socially. On one of these occasions, she asked me if I would dine with her and the film-star, Robert Mitchum, because he had a request to make of me. Naturally I accepted the invitation; I assumed that the only thing Mitchum could possibly want from me was a film script. Little did I know. I remember we dined in one of those *chi-chi* restaurants where you can never see what you are eating, whom you are cutting, or what you are paying. This one had been cunningly carved out of a derelict church. The kitchen in the crypt, we sat in the sacristy. Like all American film-stars, he ordered caviar which, to my palate and pocket, is only redeemed by lemon from being as inoffensive as a bloater paste. Whatever was in Mitchum's mind was being kept for the coffee. Observing his nervousness, I added another nought to my fee. When the liqueurs had been set before us, Mitchum got to the point. He had great charm: I felt it beam on me like a lighthouse. 'Duncan,' he said. 'Our friend, Janet, tells me you're the one man to help me. . .'

'Oh, I don't know,' I said modestly and wholly irrelevantly. 'There are at least two other writers in this county. . .'

'Janet says you've a pedigree herd of Ayrshires. . .'

'And it's some time since I did a film script. . .'

'And I'm in a bit of a spot, you see, I'm farming and have an Ayrshire herd on one of my farms. . .'

'My last was for Gaby Pascal, you know?'

'And I can't get a licence to import the right bull. So I thought I'd smuggle in a thermos flask of your semen.'

'You mean my bull's?'

'Sure. . .'

On another occasion, Janet begged me to drive over to luncheon to meet an old friend of hers, if of nobody else — Evelyn Waugh. Like everybody, I had had a tiff with Waugh. We had not met, but I had recently written to him to try to persuade him to write a play for the Royal Court Theatre. Novelists, such as Angus Wilson, had responded to a similar

120

invitation. I had suggested we should meet. Waugh had replied on a postcard – without an envelope— from White's of course, briefly to the effect that 'I don't want to write a play and certainly do not want to meet you'. With this little squib of deliberate rudeness in mind, I told Janet that I would certainly drive over for luncheon as I was looking forward to dropping olives or peanuts down the tortoise shell ear trumpet which I'd heard Waugh sported. She said that she knew she could always rely on me to misbehave myself.

When I reached the house, Waugh had not arrived. He had succeeded in being conspicuously late. Our hostess delayed luncheon till he appeared, bearing his bloody trumpet before him like an emblem in the ceremonial entry of *Aida*. I observed that he did not use this gadget to enable him to hear, but to avoid hearing. I envied his advantage.

When Janet introduced us, Waugh indicated that he had not previously heard of me; to which gambit I replied by assuming he was his brother, Alec. We eyed each other from our corners like a couple of extinct dinosaurs surrounded by bantams. This behaviour was very silly on both our parts. I had always admired Waugh as a writer. He, Maugham and Graham Greene were the only three contemporary novelists I enjoyed. I approved of his lucid, unadorned style. I shared many of his sympathies and loyalties. To my surprise, I learned years later that he had some admiration for some of my work too. But neither of us would acknowledge the other. We sat down on the right and left of our hostess and, like the late Lord Salisbury, 'never spoke *across* the table.'

My irritation at the sole advantage his ear trumpet gave him was heightened when Janet whispered to me that Evelyn had telephoned her that morning to tell her he was on a strict diet. She had provided it. I doubted it's medical background, when I observed that he was served with shell fish. I wasn't. However much I admired his prose, I found it impossible to forgive such greed. I began to suspect that his tankard contained champagne, mine held only lager.

We parted without acknowledging each other.

A few weeks after this trivial episode, Janet asked you and me down to Somerset for a ball she was giving to celebrate her daughter, Jane Campbell's, engagement. You wanted to go because the card stated that a West Indian band had been engaged. Ever since you'd made that film in the Virgin Islands you'd liked this type of noise.

We travelled down from Paddington with my dear friend, Mike Ansell. Not surprisingly you took a great liking to each other. So cleverly does Mike always hide his disability that we'd reached Reading before you noticed that he was blind.

The evening which ended badly, started worse. Janet, remembering you were a film-star, had us shown to a room banked with flowers and floored with white rugs. As soon as the door was closed you glared at me indicating the double bed. We were of course going through one of those periods when you played the nun, or insisted that I was Rose Marie's husband and because she was your friend . . . therefore . . . etc. Or maybe we'd decided not to see each other any more and had concluded that not making love was all a part of that arrangement.

'You promised me if I came down here with you we'd have separate rooms,' you said.

'I didn't.'

'You did.'

'Don't be silly. Janet's got a large house party. People have to pig in.'

'Are you calling me a sow?'

'I am saying that having slept with you in a single bed a few hundred times I shall now be able to keep my distance in the double.'

'You can't sleep in the bed.'

'I can do worse than that. I'll show you I can sleep in that bed. My snores alone will interfere with you. . .'

And so on, if I remember, and I do remember. We didn't squabble very often. Even so, you wouldn't go down till I'd passed your appearance. You never had any confidence in clothes unless you were dressed in rags, urchin that you were.

'Do I look all right, 'iggins?' you used to say.

And if I'd said no you'd have crumpled and cried. . .

We sat at Janet's table. Almost immediately a large man approached and dragged you off to dance. I sat talking to Janet

122

trying not to hear the noisy West Indian band. Fifteen minutes later, you limped back, angry and dishevelled.

'I don't know who the hell that was,' you exclaimed kicking your shoes off, 'but he couldn't dance.'

'That was Norman Mailer, dear,' Janet said a trifle icily. 'Jane's fiancé. That's why I'm giving this party, to celebrate their engagement, you know.'

'Isn't he an actor?' I said trying to cover your gaffe, but not exactly helping.

Janet had not been amused. Three years later she might not have been offended.

We too wandered off to see if we could be less offensive elsewhere. Then, in an alcove, away from the other guests, we ran into Evelyn Waugh sulking in a quiet corner with a magnum of champagne on one side of him and his timid wife on the other. He looked cross-eyed with boredom. I believe he thought, or hoped, that I had sought him out. Reluctantly he offered us a glass of wine. Then wrapped himself, as it were, in the mantle of his fame, and lit a cigar to prepare himself for the tedium of giving an interview. Perhaps he genuinely thought I was a journalist. It's possible he thought everybody was a journalist. I decided to punish him. I sat down, drank more than half his wine and for a whole hour talked pleasantly to his wife whom I knew ran a small herd of dairy cows. I never addressed a single remark to him. He became restless, fidgeting and indignant. When we left their table he resembled one of those fish which blow themselves up to frighten off predators. But his wife was grateful for my attention. It may probably have been the first time anybody had noticed her, at least in her husband's company. But I came to regret this incident. I never met Waugh again. As I said, I much admired him as a writer.

Some weeks after Rose Marie had disappeared and while I was still living at Orme Lane, Briony had had what I thought was a bright and helpful idea. She suggested that since I was unlikely to return to Welcombe to live alone, and since Roger was at school, and she at a secretarial college, I should divide Mead up into three flats for summer lettings. I could see immediately that this would help me financially and left her to work out the details which she did most efficiently, organising the flats with the erection of only one partition and an extra bathroom. These places were quickly booked up since the house stands only a quarter of a mile from the sea.

But when the summer came these arrangements proved less satisfactory than they had originally appeared. I suppose I had failed to realise that somebody would have to be present to see the tenants in and out. Most of the bookings were for a week or a fortnight. This meant I had to return to Welcombe. But I had omitted to retain a perch for myself. So, although I owned several houses, I was driven to erect your ridiculously small tent in a paddock and play at being a boy scout in it. There was, you remember, only room in the damn thing for a single sleeping bag and it was too low to stand up in.

During the spring I had been asked by the BBC to write a full length play for them. I met Michael Barry, the head of Drama, liked him and accepted the commission, promising to deliver the script by the autumn. The theme I chose for my play was the Pilgrim Fathers. I had been fascinated by the character of Governor Bradford and the diary he kept on the *Mayflower*. My aim was to show the high hopes of the pilgrims and how quickly these collapsed, both on the boat and as soon as they reached America. I had observed that the prim Puritans had carried all the germs of the diseased society they had condemned with them. I saw the play as a possible vehicle to show how each individual contains all the dregs of society within him. It was, I planned, to be the Aeneid for the United States. I called the play *Preface to America*.

As usual, I put my literary commitments last in my priorities. The spring passed while I buried myself fixing kitchen gadgets in self-contained holiday flats: I had written nothing. By June, I could see I had only two alternatives: either to write the play lying prone on your sleeping bag within my commodious tent; or, alternatively, moving a card table into the small greenhouse and using that as a sunny study. I thought this an inspired idea. It might have been in a normal year. But 1959 was a particularly hot summer. I sat sweating surrounded by wilting tomato plants. I worked hard but

124

badly. I myself was never satisfied with the play as this letter to you shows.

Beloved Urchin, My Dearest Ragamuffin, you.

For the last hour I've been sitting out here on the lawn trying to work. But I cannot. My mind is obstinately uncreative: like a blanket, like potato soup. I cannot think why: I slept well. Perhaps I'm just exhausted after my emotional crisis yesterday? Perhaps I'm just dull? But I know that now I'm only able to absorb things casually: the noise of the tractor, Tom using a pick-axe doing the crazy paving (at last); a small dead bird on the lawn at the bottom of the magnolia tree . . . but I can't re-orientate anything, write a coherent line. This Pilgrim play has died a still birth . . . I suppose I've put it away too often. It lacks immediacy; the characters are bores, their utterances are trite. And the whole thing nauseates me. At least, this morning it does. If only I didn't feel that the BBC were impatiently waiting for every page. They're not; but I feel they are. There are all sorts of agonies but one of the worst is for a writer – or any artist – to be at the bottom of his form and know it. I fell just like Pavlova with a club foot or Rubenstein with boxing gloves on his hands trying to play a nocturne.

If only I had patience: I am the most impatient clot that ever lived — when it comes to myself. With others I'm too patient.

Don't let Ezra's *ABC of Reading* make you feel illiterate. I haven't read half the books he mentions. Nor need you. But he does establish certain values and avoid some prejudices which make the book useful to *glance* through. I shan't let anything intimidate you. Will look out some more homework for you during the day. And when we next meet, we'll chatter about some composers and poets until you are as ignorant as I am. You know, I daresay, I've read even less than you have. The only thing I've done consistently is to smoke. But I want to lead you to like the things I love for no other reason than that I love you too. How easy it is to love you. I wish I could write as easily as I can love.

I am worried about Bunny. Her eyes are very painful.

Yesterday I spoke to Dr Holtby. He said that unless she rested, her eyes would get worse, become ulcerated and she might even lose her sight. I have decided that the only thing I can do is to frighten her into resting. It would be cruel of me not to warn her.

I feel a little clearer now — writing to you quietly like this has been so effortless, it's rested the tempest of me.

Antonia writes asking if she and Leo can go to the Hermitage for a week. She offers to clean the place up ready for the guests in lieu of rent. I can't think of any reason why I should refuse them. It's so sad to see everything empty and not a giggle anywhere.

Did I tell you Basil Ashmore waylaid me at the Garrick? He wants to start up High Wycombe Rep with my Judas play. Why? He hasn't even read it.

I shall phone you this evening.

When we go to Oxford I want to buy you a pretty summer dress.

The sun's gone in, so will I. I will go and cook my lunch — 2 gulls eggs.

Arab

Perhaps because I had written it in the greenhouse the play was literally half-baked. Somewhat to my relief the BBC decided not to produce it, not because they detected its failings, but because, as so often happens there, the person who had commissioned this work was no longer there by the time it was completed. What they call their 'policy' had changed. Every broom has to be seen to sweep, at least for a time.

During this summer I received a request from ABC television to turn my play *Saint Spiv* into a musical for television. This was the play which Kenneth Tynan had directed at the Watergate. I had, at Eliot's request, changed the title, which he'd found offensive, to *Nothing up my Sleeve*. The play had only run for a month or so. I thought it had been forgotten. I had regretted this because the Chaplinesque characters of 'Orace and the street *gamine*, Penny, appealed to me. But the idea of turning this play into a musical didn't attract me. Musical comedies nauseate me: I have always found their

126

lyrics banal, their melodies corny and their dramatic situations as subtle as a ham sandwich. I met Ted Kotcheff, who wanted to direct the piece, and Peter Luke, the producer, at Teddington. I told them of my musical apprehensions. They tried to reassure me by telling me that the composer, Matyas Seiber, had already agreed to write the score if I approved. I had not heard of Seiber and was therefore guarded. But I agreed to accompany them down to his house in Sussex a few days later to discuss the matter. Meanwhile I hurried to George to ask him if he had heard of Seiber. He, of course, had. He thought highly of him and told me that a Seiber piece was being played that week by the London Symphony Orchestra in a Prom concert which included Tchaikovsky's violin concerto and Fourth Symphony. He suggested I went along to hear Sieber's work before our meeting. I did this and was very impressed. When we met again at his cottage, he played several sketches he'd composed for the proposed musical: these were very promising, in the line of Kurt Weil, not Rogers and Hammerstein, Novello and Slush.

Everything was agreed. I became enthusiastic: a chance to write something like *The Threepenny Opera*, I thought. You could play Penny. I began to write the script when I heard to my sorrow that Seiber had been killed in a motor accident in South Africa. Other composers were suggested. But I lost interest and never completed the script.

Besides, television had let me down, and you, too often. We were both disenchanted with it. There had been that disastrous production of my play, *The Death of Satan*, in which Wilfred Lawson had been recklessly cast for the lead. Lawson was a very good actor, and perfectly cast for the part of Satan. But Lawson had a problem: he was seldom sober. Certainly he was too drunk to get through the dress rehearsal and was clearly on such a bender that the director could see it was not possible for him to play before the cameras that evening. John Laurie took the part. With less than eight hours rehearsal he gave a very creditable performance. Indeed his contribution was the only thing I liked in the production.

At this time, I had become involved with William Sassoon. He had had considerable success as a film producer in Paris with such actors as Jean Gabin. He had approached my agent, Margery Vosper, to enquire whether I could solve a problem for him. Apparently he had acquired from Roland Petit the dramatic rights of one of Petit's ballets which ended in a strangulation scene on a bed in a cheap hotel. The ballet lasted fifteen minutes, the strangulation scene less than one. Sassoon offered me £500 if I could think of a play which could lead to the ballet and end with the strangulation scene. The problem intrigued me. Rose Marie became fascinated by it too. She helped me to concoct the synopsis, called *The Preying Mantis*. I thought it ingenious and handed it to Sassoon who was enthusiastic and paid my fee. He sent the synopsis to Petit.

I heard no more of this project. That was the end of that. A writer's life is mostly like that: approaches which waste your time, sketches which take your time; ninety per cent of it comes to nothing more than talk. But Sassoon was a persuasive man. He was no ordinary film producer; he was a somewhat impecunious member of the banking family with the looks and manner of a distinguished diplomat. He was grasshopper-like with his enthusiasms but they generally alighted on me.

His next approach after the sudden demise of *The Preying Mantis* was a request that I should make an English version of Marcel Achard's play, *Au Claire de la Lune*. Achard had been associated with Sassoon in Paris and this was his most famous play. Sassoon told me that Achard had already agreed to my making this version and I said I would accompany him to Paris to meet the dramatist. But Achard's wife came too. The four of us had luncheon at the Mediterranean. Madame Juliete Achard clearly ran her husband. Her conversation was only interrupted when she paused to light another cigar. I felt so sorry for Achard that I agreed to do the adaptation which I called *The Comedy of Lovers*.

It has never been produced. I don't suppose I could find a copy; but it was, you'll admit, another thing I wrote for you.

As George said: it could only have happened to me. But it did. My play, *The Death of Satan*, was presented in New York. The management had great hopes; I, having been round this

128

thorn bush before, was less optimistic. But even I was surprised to learn that the play had had to close because my two leading ladies had eloped, leaving Don Juan alone on the stage. A week or two later they turned up at the de Vere Hotel in Kensington and asked me to breakfast, presumably a wedding breakfast. Their purpose in wishing to see me was to thank me for writing the play without which they would not have been brought together. I have seldom seen a happier couple.

Part Three

The Pit

By the autumn of 1960 Rose Marie and I were sufficiently reconciled for me to suggest that I should take her and the children to Brittany for a holiday. I felt nervous about this. I told you that I was doing it for the children's sake. My reason did not impress you, as a postscript to one of your letters indicated. In this you referred to Gretchen as The Evil Eye. And threatened to 'tear her hair out' if she prevented Rose Marie from going to Brittany. You hoped that Rose Marie would be firm. And you went on to reassure me that you didn't think that my going to Brittany with Rose Marie meant that I loved you any the less. Perhaps more, you said, for it showed the trust between us. But there was one thing you would not let me get away with: that was my using the children as an excuse.

You thought it was perfectly natural of me to want to go on this holiday and assured me that you had no misery about it. This was typical of you. And what did you do a few days later? You marched me in to some emporium in Shaftesbury Avenue which specialised in casual holiday clothes. 'You're going to look smart and be a credit to me,' you had said. 'I'm not having Rose Marie say I've sent you off looking scruffy.'

Consequently when Rose Marie and Briony met me at the airport they were pleased. They could see someone had made an effort. Naturally they didn't give me the credit.

It was a happy and successful holiday. We drove round the coast feasting on *moules* and oysters. Roger and I slept in a tent, Briony and Rose Marie in a hotel. Perhaps because I wished you were with us, I carried a primus stove, a frying pan and a saucepan in the boot. The best meal I ate was when we bought a kilo of prawns and boiled them, squatting in a ditch.

After the sad fiasco of the previous year you decided rightly to avoid a possible repetition this Christmas. To make it easier for me not to spend it with you, you said you'd agreed to go to stay with your mother at München Gladbach in Germany and therefore you suggested that I should invite myself to Rose Marie's flat at Hamilton Terrace. Briony would be there and Roger, too, who had decided to earn some pocket money during his holiday by working in Marks and Spencer's where he was persistently teased for his Fortnum and Mason accent. This plan seemed to be sensible until we came to part, whereupon we both literally fell to pieces. The tears squirted out of you at right angles to your eyes. And we were only being separated for ten days. But what had made you cry? Was it the little present Rose Marie had wrapped up so prettily and given me to hand to you? You had bought a present too. Gestures like these made it quite impossible for me to restrict my affections to either one or the other of you. I had, I suppose, written *The Catalyst* only to become *The Catalyst*. Whatever I had done I missed you. I hid these feelings under a paper hat. And I remember sending you a poem every day.

> Today, I am sad,
>   sad as stone things are
> In their stillness;
>   or as old toys are
> In their loneliness;
>   as a room is
> That is empty;
>   as a child is,
> That is lost.
> This sadness clothes me
>   as sparrow feathers
> Fit a sparrow's wings;
>   closely it lies over me
> Completely like a panther's skin
>   over the panther,

134

Giving its savage stealth
        the quiet sheen of night.
So do I walk, wearing your absence
        like a crimson robe:
Proud of my grief, Prince of our parting.
Let others be beggared in gaiety,
        I will sit here rich in my waiting,
Quiet in my wanting.
        Clothed in this sadness I wear
What you have woven;
        my silence speaks:
All time shall hear
        what this dumb heart has spoken.

An uncle of mine had died in London. He had been my mother's eldest brother and had lived in South Africa for thirty years. I learned that his sole bequest to me was a sealed cigar box. Naturally, I wondered if it was full of sovereigns; and you hoped it contained diamonds. I collected the cigar box and carried it to my room in the Cumberland Hotel where I was staying at the time. Once alone, I clawed at the seal and undid the *heavy* box. I was convinced it was gold. He'd lived outside Johannesburg, on the Rand. But there wasn't a single coin inside: just a revolver with six live cartridges. I picked it up and loaded the thing. What did this bequest imply? Russian Roulette? That he knew his nephew deserved no less, or would in time need nothing more? I was both disappointed and frightened. I was too unhappy, too open to acute depression to relish owning this damn thing now in my hand. So easy to do it. Not even I could miss. I hurriedly shoved it back into the cigar box and put it under the dashboard in my car. An hour later we were driving somewhere and I showed you the box. You were delighted, thinking it was another water pistol, far more fun than diamonds. I showed you that the cartridges were real. We pondered why my uncle had made this bequest but came up with no answers. I resolved to sell the damn thing to a gunsmith even if I only got £10 for it.

Having dropped you at the studio, I drove to a well known gunsmith in Mayfair to ask if they would be interested in buying an almost new automatic revolver. The assistant said he would be, but could not purchase it unless I first produced a police licence for owning the gun. He advised me to drive immediately to the Police Station in Savile Row to deal with this formality.

The officer produced the requisite form and began to complete it. How had I obtained the gun? I had inherited it. From whom? That, too, was easily answered. Had he had a licence? I didn't know or care but could see that a summons would not inconvenience him now. What was the number on the gun? I asked the officer to wait while I fetched it from the cigar box beneath the dash board. The box was still there. I carried it into the station and opened it before the sergeant. The box was empty. He did not appear amused.

'It must have been pinched from my car.'

'Outside the Police Station, Sir?'

'Could have been outside the gunsmith's.'

'You admit to having the gun. Unless you can produce it we shall have to institute careful enquiries.'

'I don't doubt,' I said, fleeing, after scattering all my, your and Rose Marie's addresses to confuse him.

That night I waited up for you but something had gone wrong with your schedule and eventually I went to bed at 2 a.m. I let you sleep the next morning and woke you with some tea half an hour before the studio car collected you again. You asked for a cigarette from your handbag. I opened it to stare at the missing revolver.

'So you're the bloody thief,' I cried. 'What did you take it for?'

'It was great fun. Don't be cross. I've been firing it at half the people on the set and scared the life out of one or two cameramen besides. Don't take it away from me.'

I opened the gun. It was still loaded. Feeling sick, I removed the single cartridge which I myself must have left in the bloody thing.

'And to think all those film-stars are still alive!' I said.

I drove back to Savile Row deciding to tell the officer that I had found the revolver under some gloves in the dash board. But before going into the station I parked the car in Hanover

Square with the purpose of losing the cartridge. I idled over a gutter. Some damned pedestrian stopped to tell me I had dropped something. I picked the thing up again and looked for a litter basket. Couldn't find one. Pop it through a letter box? Swallow it? In the end I got on a bus in Oxford Street, and left it on the seat. Then I entered the Police Station again and gave myself up, as it were. The Sergeant wrote out my licence. I left it and the gun on his desk. I had had enough. I believe he had too if his look was anything to go by.

It was you who had insisted two years previously that I should see Rawle the psychiatrist. Since then I had had two or three hourly sessions with him a week. I continued these even after I discovered that Rawle was not the well known psychiatrist I believed him to be but that he bore the same name. I went to him because Rawle had impressed me; he was intelligent, broad-minded and sympathetic to my situation; also he admired my work and when a man did that of course I always thought him intelligent. He was a poet himself and though his work was of no considerable literary consequence, it showed his sensitivity and, I thought, revealed sufficient pain in him to understand mine. You and Rose Marie too, were also seeing him regularly. We each learned a little about each other's feelings, perhaps just sufficient to prevent us from treading on them. In these sessions I learned something about myself too: that I had a tendency to martyrdom and used that to punish other people; that my kindness was often most unkind; that one of my worst faults was my inability to release my anger against anybody but myself. These were things worth learning about myself and later I projected these attributes into the character of Christopher in *The Seven Deadly Virtues*, a play which was eventually staged very briefly at the Criterion. I also learned how much you resented the fact that I had never written a play for you although you had acted in *The Catalyst*. I rectified this by writing *The Urchin* for you immediately. And a few months later *Abelard and Heloise*.

We all became very dependent on Rawle. Talking about oneself becomes an addiction. But unhappily he often let us down either by arriving late, or frustrating us further by failing to keep an appointment. George eventually persuaded me to go to Metman, a friend of Jung, whom he consulted himself; while Marion suggested that you went to her psychiatrist, a woman. You agreed; it was this decision which eventually undid us. Decisive steps are seldom taken consciously.

When you were at Mead helping Rose Marie with her summer letting the year before, you had asked me to give you driving lessons. I had already taught you how to ride. But you didn't take to a car so easily. I used to put an upended match box on the dash board, then scold you when ever you let the clutch out roughly and knocked the box over. You took your lessons very seriously. When you returned to the studio you took a driving course. I often noticed that the ability to learn to drive a car has a profound significance to a girl. It was so in your case. I dare say there is some psychological reason. The motor must be symbolic to them. Perhaps it signifies freedom, or their emotional drive. Certainly, for young men, the motor is a sexual sublimation or compensation. And with you, the ability to drive was of great consequence. You decided to take your test in Barnstaple because you'd been told that it was easier to pass in the country than in London. You came to stay at Mead for the occasion. When we drove into Barnstaple on the fateful day, you were much more nervous than before a first night of a play.

I sat in a café waiting apprehensively while you had your test. We'd arranged to meet at the clock tower near the bridge at mid-day. When I met you you were already waiting, sitting on the pavement howling your eyes out. You had boshed a three point turn, crashed your gears and failed. I picked up the remnants of you and made you drive me home without a licence to try and give you back some of your confidence.

After two more tests you eventually passed. You were never a good driver: you always took corners too fast, braked too late, then too fiercely. You always assumed yours was the only car permitted on the road. Indeed you had learnt too much from me. But to celebrate your getting this automobile Oscar (you used to flash your driving licence at me as though it was a PhD) you bought a second-hand car. Then you applied for insurance and discovered that, since you were an actress, the premium would be very high as your profession is considered the worst possible risk. So your car was transferred into my name. I insured it. You drove yourself down to the studio every day and in the evening played at being my taxi.

I was sitting in Rose Marie's flat in Hamilton Terrace where I had been invited for morning coffee when the telephone rang. Rose Marie returned to the room very white. 'I have some bad news for you,' she said gently. 'That was Virginia's film studio; she has turned her car over on the icy road. She's got concussion. She's calling for you. You must go immediately.'

Your car was a write-off. But you'd escaped with no more than a bad bump. You were conscious and tearful when I arrived. Your nerve was completely shattered. The production company was distraught, no shooting could go on without you. After a week the doctors said you could go on the set again. You refused unless I stood in the wings to give you confidence. Consequently the management telephoned me in London to ask whether I would come down to stay at Pinewood if they paid all my expenses and I just stood around. That's what I did. Somehow this film was finished. I can't remember its name. I can remember standing there in the wings watching take after take and then, at the director's urgent request, coming almost on to the set so that he could get something into the can.

As if I had not enough life of my own, I now became involved in Oscar Wilde's. Two films had been made almost simultaneously about him. *The Evening Standard* commissioned me to write a serial based on the script of one of these films which depicted his trial and cross examination. I enjoyed writing this. Wilde had always appealed to me as the only real wit since Rochester. I had always admired *De Profundis*, *The Ballad of Reading Gaol* and *The Importance of Being Earnest*. I had always felt deeply sympathetic to Wilde for subjective reasons: he too, had been run over by that tram we call convention...

It was this interest in Wilde which had made me associate with the Queensberrys for many years. For this family, having persecuted Wilde and caused his downfall, as soon as the mad Black Douglas died, had become his champions. Francis Queensberry collected Wilde manuscripts and first editions. I had found one or two for him. Francis always kept Wilde's black Deed Box marked with the poet's name in his sitting-room. It was his most precious possession. When I had edited *Townsman*, Alfred Douglas had submitted some poems to me which I had rejected. But I was on very friendly terms with the rest of the family: I admired Katherine Mann's work. After she divorced Francis, he had married Mimi, a cousin of my oldest friend, Richard March. Their child, Gwain Douglas, had been brought up at Bude; he used to cycle over to Welcombe sometimes bringing a short story he'd written for me to read. It was odd seeing him about Mead since he'd grown into a replica of his uncle; fortunately only in appearance.

As soon as the first instalment of my Wilde series appeared, other ghosts from his past whom I had mistakenly thought dead, emerged from their shadows. Wilde's son wrote, and so did some of the poet's friends. I became enmeshed in this correspondence. But this interlude had its consolations. As he might have said: it is only when we contemplate other poet's lives that we see how well they have mis-spent our own.

Rose Marie, free from the responsibilities of Welcombe, had taken up her drawing again. I have never met an artist who took her work less seriously, perhaps because she was so naturally gifted. Where others have to labour, she could rely on that innate talent she was given, and never had to acquire. As with her looks, so with her ability: she was favoured, spoilt. She would do a few drawings about three times a year and then not bother again until someone persuaded her, asked to sit for her or, like myself, bullied her. She was now doing a series of portraits because I had arranged for her to hold an exhibition at the Woodstock Galleries in the new year. Ben sat for her: I think it is his only portrait. Her work was entirely ignored except by a few discerning friends such as Ben, Topolski and George. My own admiration for her work counted for nothing. She never believed it was genuine: and when I praised her I was generally in danger of being accused of patronising her. Let others judge.

I had always wanted to get to Vienna, if for no other reason than to see Schubert's house. But somehow I never managed. So when the Burgtheater there asked me to go to the opening of my play, *The Death of Satan*, I flew over to attend the last few rehearsals.

The day after I had arrived, I was sitting in the stalls with the producer watching the opening scene between Oscar Wilde, Byron and George Bernard Shaw; the stage doorman crept up to me in the dark and whispered that there was a man there who wished to see me. I knew nobody in Vienna and assumed it was a journalist.

'Tell him I'm engaged,' I said. A few minutes later, the doorman loped up the aisle again.

'He says he is not from a newspaper. He's a personal friend.'

'Then go and ask his name.'

He returned again almost immediately.

'His name is Alban Berg' the doorman said.

'Who?' I exclaimed loud enough for them to hear on the stage. I knew that the composer of *Wozzeck* had been dead for years. I thought it must be a joke, not in the best taste.

'Tell him to go away,' I said, but as the man turned away, I remembered that a few years previously, Erwin Stein, Marion's father, who had been a pupil of Schoenberg's, had introduced me to Alban Berg's brother at a Mahler concert at the Albert Hall. After it, we had all dined together and I had then driven Erich Berg back to his hotel. I recalled that he'd told me then that Alban's death was due to medical negligence.

So I got up and followed the man to the stage door. The brother stood there waiting.

'I knew you wouldn't remember my name,' he explained modestly, 'so I sent in Alban's. I thought that would fetch you.'

'I'm in the middle of a dress rehearsal,' I said. 'Let's meet for supper.'

'No,' he replied. 'It's urgent: Alban's widow heard you

141

were in Vienna. She has sent me to take you to her immediately.'

'We've never met.'

'I know. But she insists that you're the one person who can help her, I've got a car outside. It won't take half an hour.'

As we drove through the city I wondered what Alban Berg's widow could want from me. Erich looked fairly prosperous. The car was new. I doubted if it was money.

'She must be quite old,' I said.

'Seventy-nine.'

We drew up at a respectable but severe looking house which was divided into flats.

Frau Berg sat bolt upright on a wooden chair which was the only piece of furniture in the room apart from a concert grand piano. She wore a fur coat and held a walking stick. She wore an immaculate wig and the same regal and forbidding appearance as Queen Mary had had and, like her, she made me feel like a schoolboy on the mat.

She scrutinised me in silence until her brother-in-law had left the room.

'When I read in the papers that you were in Vienna I knew you would help me. We're kinsman you know. You're a Wittlesbach by blood. I am the Emperor Franz Joseph's natural daughter: so we're cousins.'

I nodded vaguely.

'In an intimate matter like this, I know I can trust you to help me.'

She got to her feet. 'But now you're here, you'll want to see my treasures. Then we'll get down to business.'

She stalked regally to the piano stool, opened it and produced to my astonishment half a roll of lavatory paper. She handed this to me. I kept a wary eye open for a white rabbit with a large watch.

'Look at it,' she said. I unrolled the stuff.

It was a musical score. Stave bars marked over the perforations.

'Schoenberg's last composition,' she announced.

'He must have been taken very short,' I said, rolling her

142

treasure up. Then she handed me some of Berg's manuscripts and tried to make me understand how these two composers had enjoyed their work.

'For them it was all great fun. All a game. Life itself was a game.' Then sadly she returned to her chair. 'And now you must tell me how I can stop the vandals.'

'From doing what?'

'Cheapening the love which Alban and I had between us. It was a great love. You would understand that.'

'How?' I asked now wondering whether I was getting smaller and smaller.

'By going to Munich on your way home and using your authority and name there to stop them.'

I tried to think of anybody in Munich who might have heard of me, but couldn't think of anybody. I sat down hopelessly on the precious piano stool. This wasn't getting either of us anywhere.

'Tell me precisely,' I said slowly, 'what exactly it is that the vandals in Munich have done or are doing.'

'Don't you know?' she asked incredulously.

'That's what I was trying to indicate, Frau Berg.'

'They have got hold of all our love letters, every one Alban wrote me, every one I wrote to him. And they're going to publish them in their entirety. It is a shameful breach of privacy. You must stop it.'

'How did they obtain the letters?'

'I had shown them to a publisher in Vienna and was considering allowing him to publish a few which referred to Alban's and Schoenberg's compositions. But now I hear that the whole intimate correspondence is to be published in a pirated edition in Munich next month. As my kinsman you will help me.'

I pondered the matter with some relief. At least there was now no walrus or carpenter standing behind her chair.

'Issue an injunction,' I said remembering that this was the legal trick André Obey, the French dramatist, had played on me twenty-four hours before the *Rape of Lucretia* had opened at Glyndebourne. Without previous warning, his injunction was issued because he believed Britten and I had plagiarized his text of *Le Viol de Lucrece*. We hadn't. But since the curtain was due to go up we could only agree to half our royalties. . .

'What is an injunction?'

I explained patiently. 'There must be some equivalent in Austrian law,' I said. 'You should go straight to your solicitor and issue an injunction against the publishers in Munich, forbidding publication. The matter will then come before the courts. It will be revealed that the publishers have no rights. The copyright of your letters to Alban belongs to you; his letters to you must belong to his musical executor.'

'Which is me.'

'Then you hold all the cards,' I said. 'My advice is to act immediately.'

She stood and tapped her stick. Erich hurried into the presence.

'I knew he'd know what to do,' she said leading the way out of the flat to the car. 'We are going straight to my solicitors.'

They dropped me back at the Burgtheater.

'An injunction you call it,' she repeated. 'I issue an injunction. As simple as that.'

'Yes,' I said getting out of the car then turned to kiss her hand. She was one of the most dignified women I ever met. Her gratitude was restrained: I recognised that we both shared a similar kind of arrogance. Blood is thicker than either hock or soda water.

One of the advantages of being absent-minded is it makes libel less likely. Though I've sat here for the last hour I cannot remember that Irishman's name. All I can recall is that he fell in love with you when he saw you on the stage in Cork almost a year before. You told me he'd attended every performance and indulged in a *blitzkrieg* of roses. I had also gathered that he was young, handsome, unmarried and rich. His hobbies were horse-breeding and ski-ing. In all, his attributes appeared attractive enough to irritate me, if not sufficient to interest you.

After you had returned from Cork enormous bouquets of expensive flowers were delivered – generally to me at Carmel Court. It was clear to us that you were being wooed. And his

144

letters, which we always read together in bed, promised you everything including matrimony.

'He's a proper gent,' you used to say. 'Not a sod like you who takes everything from a girl and doesn't even get up to get her breakfast.'

His letters began to bore you. On two occasions you found him sitting on your doorstep waiting for you to return from the studio. You sent him packing. Then he started telephoning you from Cork two or three times a day. These calls were frequently irritating. Lying beside you, I'd hear the fellow droning on and on. Your evasive replies shocked me. I found myself sympathising with this anonymous bloke. For it occurred to me that one day I might telephone you myself unaware that you were lying in bed with another man. Sometimes your acting ability nauseated, or frightened me. 'There's a whore inside every woman,' I said when you'd put the telephone down.

You clapped your hands with glee. Jealousy is the rose every woman likes to wear.

Eventually I asked you why you continued to keep Shaun O'Leary, or whatever his name was, on a string?

'I don't want to hurt him. . .'

'And you're flattered, and like our being barricaded with flowers?'

'It's generous of me to accept his presents.'

'Don't worry, you'll get a bill. There's a bill for everything.'

This one came sooner than you expected. You telephoned me at my club to beg me to go straight to the Air Terminal to meet the plane from Cork to head him off.

'What's he up to?'

'He telephoned me from Cork to say he's on his way over to fetch me. He's talking of getting married in a cathedral in the morning.'

'What do you want me to do? Give you away?'

'Be a dear and drive to the airport and prevent him from coming to the cottage.'

'I've never met him. How will I recognise him?'

'He's tall, dark, thirty. . .'

'Yes, yes, rich and handsome and he wears pheasant feathers in his hat.'

'How did you know?'

I did drive to the air terminal. But no Adonis emerged through the gate. I waited ten minutes then telephoned you to say he wasn't on the plane.

'Hurry home,' you said. 'He arrived here five minutes ago. He caught an earlier plane. Quick. Come immediately.'

'You sound as if you were about to be raped or something worse . . .'

'Such as?'

'Robbed.'

'Hurry. Please, hurry.'

I'd had considerable practice in driving recklessly. I was at Carmel Court within ten minutes. I used my latch key, stepped over Moyses Stevens' Benefit in the hall and observed Mr Leary O'Donnel seated on the edge of his chair before you. This was my first sight of the man. He was certainly young, very handsome in his tweeds; his brogues were impeccable.

You introduced us. The gentleman from the peat refused to take my hand. That was silly of him. It surprised me, it angered you.

For some awkward minutes the three of us sat like three mice before an invisible cat.

To perforate the silence, I turned to you to ask you casually what was for dinner. Of course I knew you didn't know: you never did. But it was eight o'clock and I was hungry. Yet that wasn't the reason for my curiosity. My question was deliberately framed to establish my relationship with you to this beau from the bogs. His reaction was immediate. It was as though he was a firework and my question had lit a fuse. He flung himself on his knees before you and, completely ignoring my presence and, I think, yours too, exploded into a tirade of amorous clichés: how he loved you more than life itself etc; how he couldn't live without you and that he was going to take you back to Cork that evening and marry you in the morning.

You looked startled and said nothing, but glanced at me helplessly.

'I've often wondered what a man said when he proposed to a woman,' I remarked. 'Thanks for the demonstration. I will be careful not to imitate it.'

This had the effect I intended of taking his attention from you on to myself for I could see you were frightened.

Still on his knees he turned and glared at me with admirable contempt.

'And I will rescue you from the clutches of this middle-aged lecher who's latched onto your life!'

I admired the alliteration. The Irish have an innate talent for bad poetry and poteen.

But now you were on your feet. You went to him and slowly slapped his face. Both he and I were quite surprised.

'Get out,' you said so quietly that I knew he would be well advised to beat an immediate retreat. But he didn't know you as I knew you. The poor man, having made one mistake of insulting me to your face, now made another by trying to acquire you in front of me. He produced a large sapphire engagement ring from his waistcoat pocket.

'This was my mother's engagement ring,' he announced, placing it in your hands. 'Now it is yours.'

We watched you examine the ring. You didn't hand it back to him. You threw it across the room.

It was I who retrieved it and handed it to him.

'Get out,' you said, opening the door.

He got to his feet and at the door turned.

'I will wait outside for you,' he said, 'and if you don't come to me, I will kill myself.'

'How?' was all I said.

Then he marched out and sat on the kerb opposite the cottage as he'd threatened to do.

'Do you think he will do anything silly?' you asked.

'Yes. But he won't kill himself for some years, at least.'

'What d'you make of him?'

'As you said: he's young, handsome and highly eligible. And that sapphire was genuine.'

'Be serious.'

'I think he's probably a virgin who possibly lives with another man.'

147

'He does. They've a house outside Cork. How did you know?

'From his desperation.'

'You mean his need for me?'

'No. His need is to flee from himself.'

'I suspect he's a homosexual who can't or won't accept it.'

'You mean I needn't feel responsible,' you said, going to the window.

'No, his mother should carry that.'

'She's dead.'

'Not to him.'

We saw he was still squatting on the kerb two hours later.

'Shall I go out and try to persuade him to go,' I suggested, unenthusiastically.

'No, don't you dare. He'll probably biff you one.'

'That wouldn't do at all.'

'So what shall we do? We can't remain besieged like this.'

Eventually I telephoned Rawle and told him of our predicament. He assessed the situation and said he would come and talk to the man. An hour later we saw them in close conversation on the kerb; eventually they moved off together. Rawle telephoned you to say he'd succeeded in getting your swain onto a plane by promising to plead his suit with you on his behalf.

But though I had no cause for jealousy, this Irishman's intrusion into our life, and your reactions to him, worried me. Was this unfair of me? Certainly, however you had played it, it would have been wrong: if you had capitulated to his blandishments, I would have been distraught. But you didn't; you sent him packing. Your ruthlessness, the way you threw his ring across the room, continued to disturb me perhaps longer than it distressed him. I suppose he and I had much in common: a similar desperation and need for you and a similar vulnerability to you. In a sense all men are one man, all equally ridiculous and hopelessly pathetic. And God help any of us when we kneel to a woman to find she is a wall. It was when I saw you commit him to walk the plank that I felt the rope round my neck.

148

The bouquets continued for some time. I often regretted that he didn't send champagne.

I had written my long poem *Judas* in 1957. Eliot had refused to publish it because I had 'turned the apostles into ordinary men'. He had urged me not to publish it at all. I had let it lie in my bottom drawer for several years: but E. Martin-Browne, who had originally produced *This Way to the Tomb*, liked the poem and did some readings of it with his wife, Henzie Raeburn, in the United States. He encouraged me to publish the poem. So eventually I let Anthony Blond have it. He agreed to bring out a limited numbered edition of 500 copies on hand-made paper. He was quite confident that he could sell this number at three guineas each, especially as John Piper had agreed to illustrate the poem. We drove down to Henley together so that I could discuss these illustrations with John.

I had not noticed anything strange in your mood or manner during the day. You had liked John Piper and had obviously enjoyed yourself. But that night, in a pub in Henley, marked our first division. When I went to embrace you in bed, you moved away. That in itself didn't alarm me. All women are asexual at times. But I sensed this rejection was not caused by a physical indifference but by a conscious mental veto. Nor had it arisen from a quarrel. I felt I was in bed with a nun. That was a perversion to which I was not inclined.

Your brother, Mark, was sleeping on the divan in your sitting-room. We were in the giant double bed which was not large enough for us, but now for quite another reason. Mark's presence irritated you: mine didn't seem to help either. You became moody, tearful, cold, and then, without apparent cause, suddenly gay and bawdy. I didn't know who you were. I told you so. Not unjustly you replied that I didn't know who I was either. Your moods depressed me. I thought that the cause of your misery was my refusal to make a clean break from Rose Marie, 'a decision' as your female friends put it. The vice of convention was screwed another twist. My psychiatrist didn't help. I began to suffer from migraines.

.   .   .

This summer Hutchinson's, the publishers, asked if I would write a definitive biography of Gandhi. I had, as they knew, lived with him at Segoan, and edited a selection of his writings. I needed the money and felt that I owed a great debt to Gandhi, so I accepted. I spent several weeks making notes, obtaining books from India and consulting Pyrarlal Nayar, Gandhi's amanuensis, who himself had written a biography which had been published in India but not in England. I wrote to Nehru who replied inviting me to see him. I also approached Mountbatten who was then First Sea Lord. One had only to mention Gandhi's name to get a warm response from him. He asked me to Admiralty House and offered to make his files available to me and gave me there and then a very interesting, and historically important, description of the comings and goings which led up to Indian Independence when he was Viceroy and, later, Governor-General.

I soon realised that I could not complete the biography without going both to Natal where Gandhi had practised and indeed initiated the Satyagraha movement, and also to Dehli for a considerable time to interview Nehru and many others. I could see that these journeys would cost me about double my commission fee. My agents approached the publishers asking them to cover these essential expenses. They refused. I had to abandon the book. Another two months' work went down the drain. Even so, I should one day write up the disclosures which Mountbatten had already made to me. That is, if he does not do it himself which he should; he tells it all so well.

Indecision became a disease with me. Decision, or choice, a cure I could not, would not take. You were now ill and I could see that I was your illness. So I took myself to my doctor and told him of your moods and the tears which were caused by my double life. He seemed dubious about the cause and thought he ought to see you himself. He advised me to move from your flat and to put some distance between us, if only for a time. I told him that was unthinkable: I was obsessed with you. I have never forgotten his reply. 'You're like a man who has fallen in love with one herring and refuse to believe that the sea is almost solid with shoals of this particular fish.'

I thought this very rude of him. It was of course perfectly true.

'You may be right,' I said, 'but I didn't come to you for the truth, I came for a sedative.'

He scribbled a prescription: 'There you are,' he said, 'if that's all you want.' Then he relented. 'I've got a small basement flat here. It's empty. Why don't you move in for a month or two? Neutral ground is what you need. If you were to move in here, you'll soon bring your two ladies to heel.'

I took the flat and said I would move in the following week.

But the doctor apparently knew even less about women than I did. My move hardly brought you to heel. When I told you that I'd taken this flat because my presence in yours was clearly undesirable, you became quite hysterical.

'Undesirable?' you shrieked.

'We don't even make love now. . .'

'That's only because I love you too much to make love to you.'

I had no chance to digest your paradox. You now threw yourself onto the floor in a state of uncontrolled hysterics. I tried to comfort you; I failed. You were still weeping three hours later when I undressed you to put you to bed. Something had broken. I didn't know what. You were such a good actress, I was never really sure when you were acting or when you were not. So I did nothing. But you were still crying in the morning. This wasn't a performance. I telephoned the doctor. He came immediately. I left him with you. Within five minutes he came out to me.

'She must go into a nursing home immediately,' he said. 'Where's the telephone? I'll arrange it.' He scribbled an address. 'Take her there in a taxi.'

'I've got a car.'

'I said a taxi. You'll need both your arms. She's suffering from an acute nervous breakdown. There may be other complications. Pack her things for a few weeks. I shall visit her this evening. You'd better go and dress her.'

I liked this man's decisive manner. It rubbed off on me.

Perhaps, incredibly, my first decision was to telephone Rose Marie. I told her of your breakdown. She was appalled, but not surprised. 'I'll come immediately,' she said. Intuitively I had known this would be her warm response, made from herself, before the group-values which sometimes muddled her mind could intervene. When she arrived, she comforted you, helped you to dress then packed your ridiculous wicker suitcase. She noticed that all the cushions she'd made to furnish Orme Lane were now in your sitting-room. But she managed to keep this hurt to herself.

Bethanie Nursing Home was at Highgate. You were quiet in the cab. Like a little wet sparrow being put into a cage. A nun opened the door. Why were nuns always around you? Had the doctor told you the nursing home was run by nuns? Is that why you'd agreed to go?

We were shown into a waiting room. The moment the door shut you began again to weep uncontrollably. Another nun came and led us upstairs. You were still crying. You were given a private room overlooking the garden. I stood by the window while they undressed you. When I went to leave the room you'd grown hysterical again.

They gave you a sedative. But it wasn't that which quietened you. I had packed Pedro. With him clutched in your arms, you eventually let me go.

I visited you in the nursing home at least once a day, often twice. Your condition deteriorated. You were under heavy sedation. My presence gave you little comfort. You lay there clutching Pedro. But you always wept when I went to leave. I was acutely anxious for you.

The doctor visited you daily. One day, and this of course I never told you, he asked me to go to see him. He wanted to know whether there was any mental instability, in your family. I didn't know. He suggested I found out then let him know. I telephoned one of your relatives. I gathered that a grandmother had become insane. I told the doctor; he looked very serious at this information.

I generally dropped into Rose Marie's flat in Hamilton Terrace on my way to or from your nursing home. She was sympathetic, genuinely concerned. I told her that my visits did little to comfort you, that you didn't appear to be getting any better.

152

'I'd better go to see her,' she said firmly. I was naturally very apprehensive of the effect such a meeting might have on you, especially in your overwrought condition. But I said nothing, perhaps remembering how Rose Marie had succeeded in comforting you when she'd come round to Dolphin Square.

'What will you do?' I asked fatuously.

'Tell her to pull herself together and draw her portrait.' She picked up a large drawing pad and left immediately. I remembered that when Rose Marie had been doing the series of portraits of well known actors and actresses, you had admired them and had asked me if I could persuade her to draw you. I had asked her. She had refused. This had hurt you.

I visited you myself later that same day full of trepidation. When I entered the room I saw instantly that you were now in focus. For the first time for over a fortnight, you were sitting up in bed smiling; a complete metamorphosis. Rose Marie's portrait of you was lent against the wall.

'Rose Marie's been here,' you said proudly, 'and look what she's brought me.' it was a gas lighter in pig skin. You were happy, grateful for her gesture. But neither you nor Rose Marie were aware of the significance of this particular gift. Or were you? I shall never know. All I do know is that in *The Catalyst*, I had made Leone steal Teresa's petrol lighter as a symbol of the affection she wanted from the elder woman, but had not received.

The doctor whom I telephoned thought your recovery was due to rest and his drugs. I knew otherwise. After leaving you, I called in to thank Rose Marie. She took the effect of her visit on you for granted.

'The poor kid needs affection,' she said. 'Not just masculine passion.'

I took her criticism. Well deserved.

After this, your complete recovery was almost as quick and comprehensible to me as your collapse had been. The sister told me that I could take you home within a couple of days. She was unable to hide her feelings at the thought of your leaving. She should have been pleased; her disappointment was transparent. She was an Irish nun who had mothered you devotedly.

When I did drive to Highgate two days later, I found your room empty. You had dressed and were out in the garden with this woman. I waited half an hour. She was weeping when she saw us into my car.

'What a strange effect you have on some people,' I said as we drove off, 'especially nuns.'

'Sister O'Malley and I became very fond of each other,' you said simply. 'What's strange in that?'

'Nurses surely don't weep when every patient leaves.'

'This morning she said that there's nothing she wouldn't do for me and proved it.'

'How?'

'We were in the greenhouse. She lit a cigarette. Then she said to me there is absolutely nothing I wouldn't do for you. If you asked me to burn my hand with this cigarrette, I would. And before I could stop her, she gouged the lighted cigarette out on to the back of her hand, burning it badly.'

I made no comment. But now I can't help asking you why a year later you took a lighted cigarette and stubbed it out on the back of my hand? I still carry that scar, amongst others.

Lavinia Lascelles, George's cousin, was one of my closest friends. She is the daughter of Sir Alan Lascelles who had been King George's VI's private secretary. Lavinia was a strikingly beautiful girl. Some fourteen years previously she had married Edward Renton, a promising conductor. She had had two sons. The marriage had collapsed. She now lived alone in a state of relaxed chaos in the tiny country cottage which looked so incongruous in the middle of Kensington. The cottage surrounded a grand piano: she had a pretty voice and occasionally gave a recital. She was almost as untidy as you.

I need not describe Lavinia because Somerset Maugham, unknowingly, did that perfectly when he drew a portrait of Rosie in *Cakes and Ale*. As I say, Lavinia and I were bosom friends: we cried on each other's shoulders. Though our friends suspected otherwise, we never had any other physical relationship, probably because either one or the other was always entangled elsewhere. But we were intimate and had no secrets. If I was not consoling her, she was fully occupied

154

propping me up. Neither of us had any illusions about the other. Perhaps that is why our friendship still survives. Lavinia is a woman I don't contact when things are going well. We run to each other in trouble and consequently continue to see each other frequently.

When you came out of Bethanie you moved into Lavinia's cottage at Carmel Court. She had said you shouldn't be alone. With Lavinia's care you were soon well enough to start rehearsals of some innocuous television play. I clung to my refuge in the doctor's flat and entertained Rose Marie to dinner there one evening. I even began to remember I had once been a writer and managed to find an act of an unfinished play which I had started a year or more before for the Royal Court. I found it difficult to pick the play up again. I couldn't write a line.

In this mood I consulted Tom Eliot. We had a long luncheon. I told him of my difficulties and he said he'd experienced them too. 'If you leave something you're writing for a few months and then try to continue, the problem is that you're no longer the same person that started the work when you go to pick it up again.' Sadly I agreed. I immediately found myself confiding all my emotional troubles to him. None of it was news to him. 'Of course I knew. You've been seen dining often enough in the Garrick with this girl. . .' To my surprise, though Tom had been shocked by *The Catalyst*, and had refused to publish it because of its 'immoral tone', I now found him wholly sympathetic to my own 'immoral' life. Whatever his own intellectual prejudices were, personal contact softened them.

He was relieved to know that I had resisted divorce and was still seeing Rose Marie. 'People have had mistresses before,' he said surreptitiously taking another of his own cigarettes.

As we were leaving the Étoile he asked me if I had written any poetry recently.

'Only things written as postcards to Virginia.'

'Could I see them?' he asked. 'I don't want to pry but. . .'

During the next month, I managed to find some of these poems appropriately filed by you as unpaid bills. I also retrieved two or three written to Rose Marie and sent them to Tom. He wrote to me shortly afterwards.

Dear Ronnie,

I have been mulling over your poems. Some of them I find very impressive, some of them seem to me to show the influence of Ezra in his more tiresome form and some of them I am still doubtful of for reasons personal to yourself. I feel that some of them are so good that they ought to be published and am wondering whether we could come to an agreement about a selection.

With that in view I would be glad if you could come and see me here some time, after I have read them all once again, and talk things over. Will you let me know if you are to be in town from now on and where to reach you, so that we could make an appointment for next week or the week after.

Yours ever,
Tom

And later, when he had gone through my poems again.

Dear Ronnie,

I've now been through the revised *Solitudes* and here are my views as to how the volume might be presented. I think that the volume itself should be called *The Solitudes* (which is the original title) with a sub-title 'and Other Poems'. 'The Solitudes' would actually be the first section, followed immediately by 'The Post-Cards'. I would like to include in 'The Solitudes' section all the poems which seem to me to spring from the same inspiration, including 'Letters Amorosa', 'The Warning', and 'The Plea'. After 'Post-Cards' I should put 'The Need'. 'Canzone' seems to me to belong to 'The Solitudes', as do 'Song' and 'Lute Song'. Then come the other poems: 'Strophe and Anti-Strophe', 'Impromptu for a Child', 'Solitude No. 15' which doesn't seem to me to be a Solitude at all, and possibly 'Amo Ergo Sum'; 'The Crone's Lament' certainly, and 'Air Raid' is a good poem. You might, if you like, end up with 'The Calendar'. I am returning the poems for you to run over again, and you will find one separate section of the poems which I should advise omitting. Some of these seem to me

156

just not good enough; others seem to me more fitting for another volume, and I have also in mind that we don't want a book like this to be too long. I think that with the poems which I have mentioned to be included, we shall find that the book is as long as is desirable.

Of course, I am only suggesting definitely the several sections of the book; I am not concerned here with the order of the poems within each section, to which I should like you to give your final arrangements.

I have made pencil comments on three or four points here and there where it seems to me that you need to give a little further thought. There are a few minor blemishes which could easily be removed.

When you return the poems, I should be glad if you would include a table of contents. I am always nervous about loose sheets getting out of order.

The words 'The Solitudes', once the title is given to the section, should not appear with the numerals. I don't suppose, in any case, that you intended them to be included on every page

Yours ever,
Tom

This was Tom at his best. I was lucky to have him as friend, mentor and publisher. The book went to press. Then Tom told me that he'd been advised to suspend publication because some of the poems could give Rose Marie cause to claim defamation, libel and sue for damages. 'We shall need a written clearance from your wife,' he wrote, 'for these poems, although most of them are not written to her.' I took the point and gave Rose Marie the letter. She immediately wrote to Faber's to give her clearance for publication. After such difficulties with these poems, Tom Eliot was not surprised when I finally dedicated them to my horse, Dil Fireb.

My double life did not double my expenditure: it quadrupled it at least. As usual, whenever I need to economize, I am driven to the extravagance of so-called investment to increase my income. I began to turn barns into flats and repair more cottages for holiday visitors. Rose Marie, seeing me sinking in a quag-mire of brochures, and observing that I was making a muddle of the bookings, duplicating dates, or casually pairing off the odd bachelor with a young spinster as a short-sighted if not blind date, volunteered to take over this side of my life. I swept it up from the floor and handed it to her gladly.

It was this sense of responsibility to Welcombe, the place rather than me, the person, which made her decide to return home in the spring. It was a decision which was never articulated, merely assumed. Whenever a woman does the right thing it is wiser not to draw her attention to it. Ever since Rose Marie had left me in the autumn of 1958 I had struggled to squash the divorce, break her dependence on Gretchen and generally re-establish the *status quo ante*. Having achieved this and having forced my will on the poor, long-suffering girl, I should, I thought, have been happy. But as Rose Marie and I drove home to Devonshire together for the first time for two years, I suddenly realised I was utterly miserable. I was driving away from you. Every mile clawed at my guts. I sat silent in the car struggling to hide my emotion from Rose Marie and myself. I had been so busy organising others I had omitted to organise myself. Now I found I had unwillingly made a choice which excluded myself. I could not live without you though I could exist without you.

You'd watched me get myself into this situation without reproach. You too wanted me to rescue Rose Marie from Gretchen; you, too, wanted her to go back to Welcombe, so long as you could come down there too; but I was not clear about this, nor were you. And Rose Marie didn't mention it. Perhaps she, too, believed that when a man does the right thing in an absent-minded moment it's unwise to call his attention to it. At any rate I now felt sorry for myself, guilty towards you, and guilty towards Rose Marie. I was only happy if I could have you both; it was as simple as that. I was as simple as that. I needed both hands. For me choice once again was amputation.

When we reached Welcombe I arrived where you were. We telephoned each other twice a day and wrote to each other at least once a day. Our parting was a pain. Poor Rose Marie had to bear it. She threw herself into the place and worked as conscientiously as she always did. We were gentle with each other. Perhaps she was missing Gretchen too.

That summer was an agony I breathed only with a pen in my hand: writing to you.

I used to find some excuse to get up to London every ten days or so. Sometimes you would be depressed and beg me to catch the next train. We were desperate. Your letters revealed your own obsession to get down to Welcombe: not only to me, but to Tarina, your foal; to Friday, your pig; to the place you loved because it was where we had first loved. This appeared an impossible hope remembering that only a few months earlier Rose Marie had named you in her divorce petition. It seemed, to say the least, even considering her mercurial character, unlikely that she would open her house to you again and risk repeating what had happened two years before. I thought your wish was hopeless; I tried to distract you from it by bundling up to London as frequently as I could. You used to meet me at Paddington, we'd drive straight to Carmel Court, fling our clothes off as we raced up the stairs and dive into bed like a couple of thirsty Arabs running to the oasis of each other.

These visits were brief, and passionate, our partings painful and tearful. I felt I was leaving a waif lost in London. I felt guilty because I had made you love me but failed to give you a life with me. This guilt obsessed me but even at its most intense I knew that there could be no solution for us two if it excluded Rose Marie entirely. She would have become a shadow between us; or rather my love and your affection for her would have been that shadow.

But during this summer, a definite change came into our love-making. You became virginal, not frigid; you didn't wish me to make love to you, but you said I had a need, which you wished to relieve. You would not let me enter you: to lessen my appetite, or your sense of obligation to me, you used to masturbate me. This retrogression surprised me and also confused me. I did not protest: there are many ways to love. For my part I have never known, or cared, where normality ended or perversity began. I had, too, every reason to be patient with you; I knew you were one of those women who had periods of withdrawal; and in addition to the psychological pressures of our situation, you also had some obscure hormone imbalance.

This was a great worry to you; I had first become aware of it soon after I had met you and you had complained tearfully to me about the amount of hair on your legs and arms. This tiny defect meant you refused to bathe or swim in public or take any film part which entailed such exposure. Quite irrationally you feared that this hirsute condition meant that you might turn into a boy. I weaned you from wasting money on cosmetics and the use of a razor and took you to an endocrologist who had put you into the Hammersmith Hospital for a few days for examination. They discovered there that a hormone problem existed and that you had a cist on an ovary. So with this background, I did not protest or complain about your inhibition which I thought was temporary and due to a cyclical physical disturbance.

Then, in the middle of the summer, Rose Marie took herself off to go to London for a few days. To my astonishment I learned from you on the telephone that you had had lunch together. I did not gather who had invited whom. 'I told Rose Marie,' you'd said, 'that I'd like to come down to Welcombe and that we were no longer sleeping together.'

I was silenced. So that was your purpose.

'And what did she say?' I asked eventually, urgently.

'She said I was to come down on Friday. But she wasn't going to be blamed for imposing any chastity which she didn't believe in anyhow.'

So you came, you got back briefly. You were radiantly happy to run around the place again. You'd broken a film contract to come down and now you happily delivered milk every morning to the nine flatlets at the Hermitage, occasionally picking up a tip which delighted you. But you adhered to our not–sleeping–together clause. For these few days you cast yourself as my daughter. I didn't complain. After all, I'd been your son often enough. Incest is not a taboo to worry me.

But I was disturbed a week later when I told Metman, my

160

psychologist, about your masturbating me. He appeared deeply alarmed and warned me to be careful of you. I insisted that he explained himself. He said his interpretation was that there was a strong homosexual component in your nature, that unconsciously you resented me because I was a man, that my penis symbolised my masculinity and that the act of masturbation was, for you, strangulation.

'You must be careful,' he repeated. 'This girl could kill you. As for your continual struggle between these two women, it is my opinion that neither of them are good for you. They are attracted to each other. You wrote *The Catalyst*. They are making you live it.'

After this session, I did not go to Metman again. Not because I thought his interpretation was false, but because I knew it was partially true. The three of us already partially knew it. Our tragedy was there. We knew but could not live with what we knew. We could not accept the burden of being. Of being different. Of being ourselves. Death is always there. That is what death is.

Postscript

My mind is a cheat. My mind is a pickpocket. It steals our happiness and leaves me only with the pain. Why is it I can remember our rows, the scenes and anguish of our partings, but cannot recall the innumerable happy days we spent together? Just as my mind deprives me of so much of my own childhood, so my memory now steals so much of you from me. And that is unfair and cruel of memory since memory alone is all of you that's left to me.

How many hundred times did we make love? How few can I remember? Not more than a dozen. Like leaves they came, as leaves they fall leaving no trace, my branches now gaunt and bare. Time's a ruthless wind and shears what's precious from us. Is it that my mind fails me because it fears you? And knows that if it allowed you in, it itself might be driven from me? Yes. The truth is there. So now it seems that our life together was a dream, a dream I cannot, or will not, remember. Were we like two sleep walkers running through our days hand in hand? So much seems lost; and what I lose of you makes me less than nothing to myself.

So I will force the coward of my mind to remember that happiness which is beyond recall. Those innocent ordinary days we spent, prodigal with hours, spendthrifts with ourselves. Days when the world said we wasted our time by passing our time together. And that was enough for us. Days when we unhooked the telephone, ignored the post and our appointments and just wandered off to be spectators of a world busy doing nothing the whole day through; or when we used to set off shopping to buy something as mundane as a loaf of bread or a cucumber and would return hours later without either but with two small turtles. Then to sit happily through the evening watching them swim around in your tropical fish tank. Some evenings you demanded that I take you to the flicks and we would then run to some tiny local cinema off Notting Hill Gate and you'd buy a big bag of pop corn which we'd wolf watching Laurel and Hardy. Though I can't recall a single meal of many we had together at L'Ecu de France or L'Étoile, I do remember how you enjoyed making me queue with you for fish and chips which we ate walking home in the rain. How you never, never wore a hat and when your hair was wet I used to tease you by saying it reminded me of rats' tails. Yes, that I remember, though our posh gala evenings have gone down the drain where pretensions and boredom properly belong.

How you hated being a film star, urchin that you were.

And my tethered mind like an old goat now grazes round those happy mornings when I forgot I was a writer, and you forgot you were an actress. When we'd both pretend to be waifs and strays wandering through Rupert Street Market and you'd talk broad cockney to a stall keeper till he'd let you help yourself to a handful of cherries or a toffee apple on a stick.

Oh where have you gone who was my friend? The mistress that you were I could dispense with, and indeed, did. Passion is no prince; we are more like beggars in ourselves, aching for companionship begging for alms in the gutter of our days. Sex is important; conversation more important. And we two could chatter away by the hour or sometimes sit conversing by never saying a word. And when we were parted I would run back to you if anything hurt me, just as you would always come to me when there were tears in your eyes. Oh where have you gone who was my self, my shadow, and my friend? Is there no end to grief? Why is pity so pitiless? I will myself to forget yet cling to the pain you've now become.

Some people who thought they knew you now say I show bad taste in writing so honestly about you. They would bury you with convention, entomb you with discretion, and in time forget you lived at all. They are fortunate. They cannot have your little fist banging on the pane, or the pain, of their mind as you pathetically beg to live by being remembered as the enigma, the gentle ragamuffin that you were. And some say I do your memory a disservice by referring to your boyishness or your fear that you'd become a homosexual. But what shame is there in that? Who is there who is whole? Your fears were you, your ambivalence was you. Those who never touched these parts of you, were close and intimate only with themselves. I will admit your complexity but will not allow you shame. You were whole. Their insensitivity to you, not this pen, desecrates your memory or your name.

Reading through these pages I have written, I am nauseated. They reek of self-pity. And though I believe we should show mercy to ourselves so as to be or to become ourselves, self-pity is another thing. These pages reveal my inability to assess the pain I was causing you and Rose Marie, and I don't suppose our past helped your husband's present. I was only able to record the hurt which rebounded from you both to me. I think of myself as sensitive: it appears that I am to my own feelings; but where others are concerned I move as gently as a rhinoceros. We are all indifferent to the pain we cause: perhaps that is why there is so much of it.

I will keep my promise to you. I will try to write 'the whole of our story', or, at least, that part which I know. But you must be patient. I haven't the strength to write any more now. Maybe the flood of grief decreases when it can swell no higher. Ten years have now passed since you took your life — which was my life. Which of us two is dead?

Index

140; returns to Ronald Duncan, 158ff

Eastwood, Tom, 109
Eliot, T. S., 21–2, 41, 67, 68, 82, 110, 111, 126, 149, 155–7
English, Gerald, 110

Gandhi, Mahatma, 150
Gretchen, 18, 21, 25, 29, 30, 31, 32, 36, 37, 38, 42, 48, 51, 69, 75, 86, 133, 158

Harewood, George, Earl of, 11, 13, 15, 17, 19, 58, 64, 83, 108, 111, 115, 127, 137, 140, 154
Harewood, Marion, Countess of, 13, 19, 58, 64, 83, 88, 138
Hordern, Michael, 12
How to Make Enemies, 9

Judas, 149

Kidd, Janet, 119
Kotcheff, Ted, 127

Lascelles, Lavinia, 119, 154
Luke, Peter, 127

Mailer, Norman, 123
March, Richard, 140
Maskell, Virginia, *passim*; in *The Catalyst*, 12–20, 22–3; first visit to Devon, 25ff.; first break with Duncan, 43; at West Mill, 32ff., 46ff.; second break with Duncan, 61–3; moves to Dolphin Square, 71; first Christmas with Duncan, 72; camping, 81; 'Green Cross Code', 82–3; further parting with Duncan, 101–5; opens new Café Royal, 111–12; charity matinée at London Palladium, 113; ' unfaithful in Dublin, 115–16; driving lessons, 138; accident, 139; Irish admirer, 145–9; nervous breakdown, 151ff.
Metman, psychiatrist, 138, 161
Mitchum, Robert, 120

Nayar, Pyrarlal, 150
Newhall, convent, 78–80
Nothing up my Sleeve, 126

Our Lady's Tumbler, 78

Pengilly, Bill, 106
Periton, Leslie, 36
Pound, Ezra, 22, 84, 108, 112, 125
Preface to America, 124
Preying Mantis, The, 128
Piper, John, 149

Queensberry, Francis, 140

Raeburn, Henzie, 149
Rawle, Stephen, 23, 96, 110, 115, 137, 148
Rehearsal, The, 94
Rideout, Alan, 111
Rudge, Olga, 22

Saint Spiv, 126
Sassoon, William, 127
Seiber, Matyas, 127
Seven Deadly Virtues, The, 137
Solitudes, The, 41, 114, 156, 157
Stratton, 12, 21

This Way to the Tomb, 149
Tynan, Kenneth, 126

Urchin, The, 137

Vosper, Margery, 47–8, 128

Wade, Tom, 106
Waugh, Evelyn, 120–21, 123
Wilde, Oscar, 139–40